"Are you sure I'm a stranger?" he asked.

Gideon bent forward and Marina knew he was going to kiss her. It was a gentle kiss, soft and exploratory, almost a question, as if he were unsure.

When he drew back, Marina said a little breathlessly, "I think I've met you in another life."

"Do you believe in reincarnation?" he asked.

"I've never thought about it, but.... Have we met before?"

Gideon stared down at her, his black eyes bottomless, unfathomable. "What makes you think we have?"

"There's something familiar about you," she said. "I'm certain I've seen your face before."

But she remembered nothing, not the searing pain of a lost baby and a broken marriage, not the act of betrayal that killed love—not even that love itself.

CHARLOTTE LAMB
is also the author of these

Harlequin Presents

358—TWIST OF FATE
364—SENSATION
371—STORM CENTRE
374—THE SILKEN TRAP
380—A FROZEN FIRE
387—THE CRUEL FLAME
393—OBSESSION
401—SAVAGE SURRENDER
404—NIGHT MUSIC
412—MAN'S WORLD
417—STRANGER IN THE NIGHT
422—COMPULSION
428—SEDUCTION
435—ABDUCTION
442—RETRIBUTION
448—ILLUSION

and these

Harlequin Romances

1722—FOLLOW A STRANGER
1751—CARNIVAL COAST
1803—A FAMILY AFFAIR
1938—SWEET SANCTUARY
2083—FESTIVAL SUMMER
2103—FLORENTINE SPRING
2161—HAWK IN A BLUE SKY
2181—MASTER OF COMUS
2206—DESERT BARBARIAN

Many of these titles are available at your local bookseller.

For a free catalogue listing all available Harlequin Romances and Harlequin Presents, send your name and address to:

HARLEQUIN READER SERVICE
1440 South Priest Drive, Tempe, AZ 85281
Canadian address: Stratford, Ontario N5A 6W2

CHARLOTTE LAMB

crescendo

Harlequin Books

TORONTO • LONDON • LOS ANGELES • AMSTERDAM
SYDNEY • HAMBURG • PARIS • STOCKHOLM • ATHENS • TOKYO

Harlequin Presents edition published September 1981
ISBN 0-373-10451-0

Original hardcover edition published in 1980
by Mills & Boon Limited

CHAPTER ONE

MARINA closed the cottage gate behind her and turned along the cliff path with Ruffy running ahead, his short white legs covering the ground at an amazing speed. The late afternoon breeze blew through his coat, lifting the thick white tufts of hair like ragged petals. Far out over the sea the sun was sinking into an unseen horizon, colouring the sky with fire. Gold and orange and blue layered the sea and against that flew a gull. Marina turned her face up to it, smiling. Raucously shrieking, the bird dived down to the coloured waves, only to strike into them and pull upwards again.

For a short distance the cliff path ran beside a road, little used by cars, generally only used by pedestrians, people making their way down to the rocky foreshore.

Marina walked to the edge of the cliff and stared down at the great slate blue boulders, the small pebbles sucked white by the sea, the flaring drifts of gold where celandines tumbled down the cliff to the beach.

She subconsciously heard the slam of brakes, the abrupt halting of a car some way behind her. A door crashed and then someone started running.

Marina turned in surprise. A man was tearing towards her at a tremendous pace, his long legs covering the grass as if he were in a race. She had an impression of black hair, lithe body, oddly white face.

As she gazed at him open-mouthed, he suddenly came to a stop, a few feet away, standing poised on the balls of his feet as though to lunge at her. His eyes pierced her face.

'Is something wrong?' Marina asked after waiting for him to speak in vain.

He was breathing heavily, his chest heaving under a tailored white shirt. His dark jacket hung open and he wore no tie. The black hair was thick and crisp, windtossed at the moment, ruffled in wild peaks.

'I thought . . .' He spoke roughly and broke off with a sort of groan. 'Nothing.'

She had never seen him before, so he could not live anywhere near here. Marina had lived at Basslea all her life. She had grown up in the isolated little cottage on the cliff. Everyone in the tiny community knew her and she knew everybody. It was a secure, sheltered environment, and one into which, for all her youth, Marina fitted perfectly. Most young people who grew up in this remote district on the north-west coast of England left for more populated spots as soon as they had finished school. Marina did not want to go away. She liked it here. She felt no yearning to go to London or Birmingham to find work.

Eyeing the stranger closely, she suddenly smiled. It altered her whole face. In repose she had a melancholy fragility, her small oval face pale and wistful, the fine silvery threads of her hair hanging in limp coils around her head. When she was a child her hair had been lint-white. 'Cotton head,' Grandie had called her. The colour had darkened slightly as she grew older, but it was still closer to white than any other colour.

The dark man seemed to stiffen when she smiled and the hands hanging at his side curled into balls. His eyes narrowed on her face as though her smile had amazed him. No, Marina thought in surprise! As though her smile had shocked him. Wasn't he used to being smiled at?

That idea made her look at him questioningly, but although his face was tough and harshly modelled it was not unattractive. Far from it, she thought. She could not believe anyone would find his face anything but fascinating.

'Did you think I might be going to jump off?' she asked him, faint amusement in her face.

'It wasn't funny,' he retorted, his jawline taut.

'No,' she said at once, contrite, realising that he was still disturbed by the fear he had felt when he saw her on the edge of the cliff. 'I'm sorry. I'm so used to walking along the cliff. My balance is very good and I have a clear head for heights.'

He had taken two steps as she spoke and was standing close, staring at her in a way which puzzled her, his black eyes roving over her from head to toe. It was not an insolent stare. Marina had had young male tourists eyeing her in cheeky familiarity before now, but the way this man looked at her was quite different. He had a faint glitter in his eyes.

His mouth was compressed, yet she felt he was exerting all his will-power to hold it steady, as though he were under some great strain. He was looking at her like someone revisiting a country they had not seen for years, and, oddly, Marina recognised that look because it was how she felt herself. Ever since she had set eyes on him she had had a disturbing sense of intimacy.

'Do you live here?' he asked her now, his heavy lids half veiling his eyes.

She had a curious impression that he was testing her. As he asked the question his voice had a deliberate ring and he watched her closely.

'Yes,' she said. 'In the cottage over there.' She waved her hand, but the stranger did not turn his black head to look at the distant cottage half hidden by its surrounding trees, and suddenly she felt that he had known the answer to her question. It occurred to her that he had seen her on the cliff walk before.

He half turned to stare across the sea. The sun had sunk now and the horizon was less fiercely coloured. The clouds were swept into grey masses with rough streaks of flame running between them like chiffon scarves.

'An idyllic spot,' he said, but she felt his mind was not on what he was saying. She felt that he was turning something quite different over in his mind. There was a bar of black across his forehead, his brows tense.

'In summer, yes,' she agreed.

'Winter?' he asked.

'Windy,' she laughed. 'The rain comes through

the walls on stormy nights. It's a very old house. The walls are enormously thick and when the wind blows fiercely the rain pours through them.'

He glanced down the cliff at where a bushy white tail was hunting among the rough grass. 'Your dog appears to be enjoying himself.'

'Oh, Ruffy often starts rabbits on the cliff. If he's very quiet he can sometimes get quite close before they dive back into their burrows.'

He nodded. 'You don't go down there too, do you?' His eyes skimmed the narrow, winding path worn by feet over the years. 'It looks very dangerous to me.'

'I've used it all my life. I'm quite safe on it.' Marina gave him a little grin. 'Honestly.' Turning away she moved to the top of the path down the cliffs and heard him coming behind her. Looking back over her shoulder she caught his eyes fixed on her. It gave her a strange feeling to see his head at that angle, the hard dark features almost inverted, peculiarly familiar to her. She knew she had never seen him before, yet when she looked at him she found nothing strange about him. She felt as if she had known him for years.

'Let me go first,' he said roughly.

Laughing, she shook her head. 'Really, there's no need. I'm quite safe on it.'

'All the same . . .' he said, and his hands went to her small waist, lifting her like a doll out of his path. Before she had realised what he meant to do he was in front of her, moving down the cliff. Marina followed with surprise and amusement.

Halfway down there was a grassy ledge, and almost by silent consent they both sat down on it. At the edge a patch of short-stemmed pink flowers blew in the wind. The stranger flicked a finger over them.

'Pretty. What are they called?'

'Thrift,' she said.

His fine brows rose. 'An unromantic name for such a pretty flower.'

'I suppose it is.' She had never thought about it, and her blank face confessed as much. 'There are lots of them. They grow all over the cliff paths.'

His eyes ran across the tussocky grass and gorse beyond them. 'There are flowers everywhere, aren't there? What are the white ones?'

'Sea campion,' she said. 'You must have seen them as you drove through the lanes. Campion is everywhere at this time of year.'

She had the most curious impression that he was deliberately making conversation, talking about the flowers because they were a safe topic. He looked down at the grass, plucking it with restless fingers.

'What's your name?'

'Marina,' she said, watching him. His face showed no flicker of reaction. Without looking up he said quietly: 'Marina ... child of the sea. It suits you.'

Most people who had never heard her name before looked interested or surprised or even amused, but this man had shown nothing. Marina told herself that she was letting her imagination run away with her, yet she could not suppress the feeling that he had known her name before he asked.

'What's your name?' she asked, thinking that it ought to be something very masculine and fierce.

He looked as though he ought to have had a name specially invented for him.

She felt him hesitate. Instinct told her that he did not want to tell her his name. Why? she asked herself. She stared at the hard clear profile etched against the sky. His mouth indented grimly.

'Gideon,' he said, and looked at her in sharp probing.

She met his eyes curiously. Why was he staring like that?

'Very Biblical,' she said, smiling. 'Gideon what?'

She heard the odd short sigh he gave. 'Gideon Firth,' he said in flat tones.

'Wasn't it Gideon who smote someone with the jawbone of an ass?'

He smiled then, the black eyes filled with amusement. 'He was a warrior, that's all I know.'

'Are you?' she asked, because it was precisely the sort of name she had thought he should have and she was amused.

'Me?' He drew a long breath. 'I'm a businessman.'

'Are you here on holiday?'

The black lashes covered his cheeks. He was silent for a moment, then he said, 'Yes.'

'Where are you staying?'

Again he hesitated. Then he said: 'I'm looking for somewhere to stay. They told me in the village that someone up here takes in visitors now and then.'

'Grandie does,' she said, laughing. 'That's who they meant—my grandfather. We've got a spare room at the cottage and in the season we often take in one or two guests. Married couples or two young women.'

'Is the room free now?' he asked, and again she felt he already knew the answer to that question.

'Yes,' she said.

'Do you think he would let me rent it?'

'You would have to ask him that.'

He leant back on his elbow staring at her, the wind whipping through that black hair. 'Would you have any objection if I stayed?'

'Why should I?' she asked, meeting his stare. A little frown etched itself between her brows. What was he getting at? Why should she mind if he stayed?

He shrugged and rose. Offering his hand, he took her extended fingers and pulled her to her feet. 'Shall we go and ask your grandfather?'

Marina whistled to Ruffy, who reluctantly left the burrows around which he was scampering excitedly. He sometimes showed hostility to strangers, growling and bristling. But he seemed delighted at the sight of the tall dark man, leaping up at him, licking his hands, barking. Gideon Firth bent to pat him, rubbing those long sinewy brown hands over the dog's rough coat.

Marina was impressed. If Ruffy liked him he must be safe. She trusted the dog's judgment. A few weeks ago a young man in a T-shirt and jeans had walked past her on the cliff path without her noting him. Ruffy had growled, hair standing on end. The young man had gone on, but as Marina returned along the path later he had suddenly leapt out at her and tried to grab her and pull her into the thick

shrub along the path. Ruffy had gone berserk and
the young man had fled with the snarling little dog
tearing at his ankles.

They walked back up the cliff. As they passed
Gideon Firth's car Marina stared at it with admira-
tion and surprise. It was a bright yellow sports car,
small and compact yet with very elegant lines,
streamlined for speed. She glanced at him sideways
and he appraised her face with lifted brows. 'Like
it?' he queried.

'It looks fast.'

'It is,' he said drily.

'Where do you live?' she asked him.

'London.' He made the reply curt. A faint mist
had begun to rise from the sea, hanging in veils
upon the horizon, slowly drifting in to shore. An
early moon floated in the midst of it, so pale it looked
almost transparent.

Marina led Gideon Firth up the shrouded garden
path. The mist was already dripping from branch
to branch above them, coiling around the small
cottage in pale strands. Light flowered inside the
small bow window looking over the garden.

Grandie came to the window to draw the curtains. He looked out with a smile as he heard
Marina's footsteps, then his eye passed over her and
she saw his face jerk and go rigid as he caught sight
of the man behind her.

A frown touched her face. Grandie had gone
white. He was staring at Gideon Firth as if he were
seeing things.

She turned her head to look up at Gideon, her
blue eyes asking him what was the matter.

Gideon was staring back at Grandie without expression. Feeling her eyes on him he looked down suddenly, the black eyes narrowed.

'Does Grandie know you?' she asked in bewilderment.

'No,' said Gideon Firth, and there was a dry irony in his tone. 'No, he doesn't know me at all.'

The door of the cottage opened and Grandie hobbled out, bent as usual, his short body contorted with the pain of years of rheumatism.

Gideon Firth stepped towards him, hand extended. 'Good evening, sir. My name is Firth—Gideon Firth. I understand you have a room to let.'

Grandie stared at him under bushy iron-grey brows. There was a silence. He ignored Gideon's outstretched hand. Slowly his blue eyes moved on past him to Marina. She stared back at her grandfather with curiosity and puzzled distress in her eyes. What was it? Why was Grandie looking so strange?

Her grandfather's stare delved into her face, reading the emotions etched clearly in the frank features.

After a long moment he looked back at Gideon Firth and his gnarled hand came out.

Gideon shook it gently and she realised that he was aware of her grandfather's physical pain, careful of the stiff, bowed fingers.

'We have got a room,' Grandie said roughly. 'But I'm afraid I've stopped letting it. I can't cope with visitors.'

She was amazed. Only a fortnight ago they had had a fishing couple staying with them, two men

who had been before and who spent all their time
out at sea in a rowing boat. Grandie had said to her
then what a change it made to have visitors. He and
Marina had cooked special meals for the two men
and it had been tremendous fun to cook the fish
their visitors brought back each evening.

Grandie caught her surprised face and looked
away. Gideon Firth said quietly, 'I shan't cause any
trouble.'

Again she picked up that hint of something unspoken, something of which both men were very
aware. Grandie was looking into Gideon's eyes with
a heavy frown.

'It wouldn't be a good idea,' he said.

'I need it,' said Gideon with an abrupt ring,
adding, 'A holiday. I haven't had time off for a year
and I'm in need of some peace and quiet.'

Grandie looked at him less antagonistically now,
his face uncertain. 'I don't want to be unsympathe-
tic, but there are problems.'

'I won't cause any,' said Gideon, his eyes on
Grandie.

'I wish I could be sure of that.' Grandie sounded
angry, rather bitter.

Marina caught a sudden movement in Gideon's
wide shoulders. He had almost flinched, she
thought. Grandie was being very unfriendly. She
moved involuntarily to Gideon's side and looked at
her grandfather. 'I'll do all the cooking, Grandie.
Honestly, it won't cause much trouble.'

Grandie turned his heavy old head to look at her
and she saw his pale mouth tighten. After a pause
he nodded, shrugging.

Gideon turned the black head to look down at her. She smiled easily at him and slid her hand through his arm. 'There you are! Grandie says you can stay. Come and see your room. You couldn't have a more peaceful view. It looks right out over the sea, miles and miles of sea.'

The cottage was very old, built in the seventeenth century of local stone, the walls twice as deep as normal to withstand the battering of gales, the windows jutting deep into the rooms with solid windowseats in them. 'Bend your head,' said Marina, laughing, because every man who came into the cottage for the first time banged his head on the ceilings.

Gideon, though, was already stooped as though in premonition of what would befall him if he stood upright. He was such a tall man that no doubt he had learnt to take such precautions.

He straightened as they went up the stairs. Marina opened the door of the spare room and Gideon walked into the room in front of her. He went to the window and leaned his elbows on the sill, staring at the darkened sea. The moon had swum out of the mists and was sending faint shafts of pale light over the waves. The tide was coming in fast, the sound of the running water and the grate of pebbles reaching them clearly.

'High tide at eight,' she told him.

'How empty the sea looks from here.' He kept his gaze fixed on the wide expanse of water. 'Do you ever get tired of it?'

'No,' she said simply.

'Never lonely?' He asked that very lightly, yet again there was that undertone of something she did not understand.

She shook her head. Gideon opened the window, the metal catch shedding a few flakes of rust. The wind rushed into the room and whipped Marina's hair into tangles, blowing it across Gideon's face, brushing his cheek and mouth, filling his nostrils with the clean fresh scent of it. He put a hand up and drew the strands away, holding them, staring at the silver glint of them in his fingers.

'Beautiful hair,' he said quietly.

They were standing very close. He looked from her hair to her and she saw the black eyes clearly, seeing the gradations of colour in the iris which separated the pupil, faint flecks of blue and yellow which at a distance were invisible but which deepened the iris to that jet black.

'Have you got any luggage?' she asked a little shyly, very conscious of the way he was staring at her.

'In the car,' he said, letting her hair drift from his fingers.

She put up a hand to brush it back behind her shoulders.

'Are you hungry?' she asked him. 'The bathroom is next door. I'll go down and start supper.'

She walked to the door and Gideon watched her without moving. Turning as she went out, she said, 'Anything you can't eat?'

'Mushrooms,' he said. 'They bring me out in a rash.'

'I'll remember,' she promised, smiling. 'Strawberries do that to me. One strawberry and I'm scarlet from head to toe.'

Grandie was in the small parlour winding the old marble clock which had belonged to his father. He looked at her over his shoulder.

'All right?' he asked gruffly.

Marina gave him a puzzled look. 'Of course. Grandie, have you ever seen him before? Do you know him?'

He turned his head away, adjusting the clock's position with great care. 'No,' he said after a pause, and she was convinced he lied. She had known Grandie all her life. He did not tell lies easily. Now she saw his ears were red. That was a sure sign.

Going into the kitchen she pulled the door to after her and began to prepare a meal, grilling bacon, slicing tomatoes and breaking eggs. It would be a simple fried meal but it would be filling. She quickly laid the table. They always ate in the kitchen because it was easier. Slicing bread, she got down the butter and put that on the table too. The kettle boiled and she made tea. The bacon was spitting and bubbling cheerfully, exuding a delicious scent. Marina broke eggs into the pan and flicked fat over them. She already had a small rhubarb crumble in the oven. It needed to be reheated, so she switched the oven on, then she walked to the door to call Grandie.

Just as her hand touched the handle she heard Gideon's voice quite clearly in the parlour.

'I know it's a risk. You don't need to tell me that. But it's one I've got to take.'

'I don't like it.' Grandie sounded furious, his voice harsh.

'I'm sorry,' Gideon said, but he sounded angry too. He did not sound apologetic. 'In the last resort it is my business, though.'

'Yours?' Grandie's voice rose angrily.

'Be quiet! Do you want her to hear?' Gideon's voice came closer. 'Is that door shut?'

'What do you mean—yours?' demanded Grandie without answering the last question. 'If Marina suspects ...'

'She doesn't.'

'You had no business coming here.'

'I didn't intend to speak to her. I told you—she was on the edge of the cliff and I thought ...' Gideon broke off, breathing thickly.

'I'm sorry. I'm sorry, lad.' Grandie's voice had altered, become softer, filled with kindness. 'It must have shaken you.'

'Shaken me?' Gideon laughed fiercely. 'I've never been so terrified in my life! I thought I wouldn't get to her in time.'

There was a silence. Marina listened, her brow creased. She had been right, then: Grandie did know Gideon and there was something between them, something that made Grandie angry. What?

She caught a sudden fierce splutter from the pan and raced to lift it from the hotplate. The eggs slid out on to the warmed plates. She served the rest of the meal and turned to call Grandie. He came after a moment and she said, 'The food's ready.'

Grandie nodded. 'I'll give Gideon a shout.'

There was no need. Gideon's wide shoulders were already filling the low doorway, his head bent. He inhaled the scent of the bacon.

'I'm starving!'

Marina smiled at him and gestured to a chair. 'Well, sit down and eat it while it's hot.' She picked up the fat brown teapot. 'Do you take sugar and milk?'

'Please,' he said, already beginning to eat.

Grandie ate more slowly, his face down. Marina pushed his cup of tea over to him, watching him. There was a worried crease between his brows and his face had a sombre look.

Glancing at Gideon she wondered what it was all about. Somehow she could not believe that whatever it was could be so very serious. Although she had only just met him Gideon had a face she trusted. The hard features were strong and confident. He was a man whose word could be relied on, she thought.

While she ate, she toyed with the problem of his age. Late thirties? Was he married? Marina knew very little about men. She had lived in this isolated cottage with her grandfather all her life and had rarely met anyone but casual visitors. She had never become friendly with any of the local young men. She had no time. What spare time she had was always spent at the piano.

Ruffy lay on the red-flagged kitchen floor, waiting expectantly for any scraps of food which were left. When she had finished her own meal Marina cut up bacon rinds for him and put them down. Ruffy wolfed them greedily. He had a passion for bacon rinds, but they had to be cut up or he would swallow them whole and get them stuck in his throat. As a puppy he had almost choked to death on one.

'I'll help with the washing up,' said Gideon.

Grandie hovered. Marina sensed a protest on his lips, but he said nothing. Gideon turned and looked at him levelly and Grandie went out without a word.

'Your grandfather's rheumatism gives him much trouble?' Gideon asked.

'Yes,' she sighed. 'I remember when I was little, Grandie used to pull up stinging nettles with his bare hands because he believed it helped his rheumatism, but it didn't stop it getting worse.'

Gideon nodded. 'It does help,' he told her. 'It's something like acupuncture. The sting of a bee has the same effect. They call it sympathetic magic, but it's based on a real effect.'

'Our doctor calls it old wives' tales,' she laughed.

Gideon smiled wryly. 'Professional jealousy.'

She looked at his long, sinewy hands. They were finely shaped, their fingers deft and delicate as they moved, fine dark hairs on the backs of them and a wiry strength in them.

'You've never had rheumatism,' she commented.

He grinned. 'No, thank God.' He was drying and stacking rapidly. She finished the washing up and dried her hands, turning to watch at he began putting the plates away. A shiver ran down her back as she realised that he was automatically opening the right cupboards and putting the things in them without asking her.

He turned, as if sensing her troubled feelings, and looked at her with dark eyes which were narrowed and probing. 'What's wrong? A headache?'

Marina's eyes narrowed. 'No,' she said, and determined to ask him exactly what was going on, but just then Ruffy seized the trailing end of her tea towel and tugged playfully at it. She laughed, pulling it away from him, and he growled, tail wagging.

Gideon had finished tidying the kitchen when she looked up again. 'Your grandfather tells me you play the piano,' he said. 'Will you play to me?'

'If you like,' she agreed without mock modesty. She liked playing and she knew people liked listening to her. She had begun to play when she was first able to sit on the piano stool. By then Grandie's hands were beginning to make it hard for him to reach across the keys, his hand span narrowing and narrowing.

She opened the door into the music room. It was the largest of the three rooms on the ground floor of the cottage. Although the ceilings were just as low, the floor space was double that of the parlour. Grandie had had two smaller rooms knocked into one years ago to accommodate the piano. It took up a large part of the room, a beautiful mellow instrument which was professionally tuned by Grandie himself. His ear was perfect, though it was many years since he had played himself. He refused to play less than superbly. The disablement of his hands had been a tragedy which had laid waste his life for years. Now he seemed to be resigned to it.

The walls were covered with souvenirs of his career, programmes, notices from newspapers, letters and signed photographs of artists he had worked with in the past.

Marina sat on the shabby green brocade stool, flexing her hands. They were her fortune, Grandie told her often, her span enormous, her fingers and wrists supple and strong. One day, he had promised her, she should go to college in London and study under the best teachers, but for the moment Grandie was keeping her with him and Marina knew she could not have a better teacher anywhere in the world. Grandie had taught her everything she knew. Music was their whole life. Grandie poured out for her the treasures of his experience and knowledge and Marina absorbed them all like blotting paper, retaining everything, learning with the speed and eagerness of fanaticism.

Without music she began to play an intricate piece of Liszt. It was her current practice piece and she did not particularly like it since it was a transcription from a Verdi opera and Marina did not enjoy music which was intended for one medium and had been transferred to another.

The curtains in the room were drawn back and moonlight made silent patterns on the trees outside. The mist at sea had thickened. From time to time she caught the wail of a ghostly foghorn like the moan of an animal in pain.

She passed from the Liszt to a piece of Chopin, her face drifting into reverie. Music made the backcloth to her life. There were few people in it. Her parents had died before she even remembered them. Her first steps had been taken with her hand in Grandie's and her first words had been imitations of his. When his own life fell into ruins around him, Grandie had left the world which had until then been his life and retired to this cottage. In winter they often saw no one but the postman cycling past the gate once a day. Most people would have found it lonely, but for Marina and Grandie it was a world enriched by music and they regretted nothing.

She sat gracefully, the silver-white hair flowing over her shoulders, her eyes on the window, unaware now of the man listening to her.

As she ended her eyes fell to the polished surface in front of her. She caught a misty reflection of a dark face imprinted behind the reflection of her own. For a second she had a fleeting sensation of *déjà vu*, frowning. Surely it was not the first time she had ever seen their faces like that, mirrored together?

She turned and Gideon sat looking at her, black eyes almost opaque in their impassivity, so that she could retrieve no shadow of a thought from their deep wells.

'Thank you,' he said softly.

The lack of extravagant praise, the quiet tone, made her blush as though he had paid her a fervent compliment. She swung on the stool, her small feet lifted off the ground, in the motion of a child.

'Do you like music?'

As soon as she had said it, her colour deepened and she looked at him, biting her lip.

'I'm sorry.'

'Why?' he asked, and suddenly his eyes were narrowed, half sheathed in heavy lids, hiding whatever expression was in them.

Marina did not know why she had apologised, only that suddenly she had felt as though she had insulted him, spoken in childish rudeness.

She spread her hands in a troubled little gesture. 'Of course you like it. I could tell.'

For a moment he was silent, then he rose and smiled at her. 'Let's play brag,' he said, and walked out of the room into the kitchen. Grandie was sitting there by the old stove which heated all their water. Gideon went to the long mantelshelf above the stove and reached up to get an old pack of cards which were always kept there. 'Brag?' he said to Grandie with a lift of his dark brows, and Grandie gave him a wry little smile.

A moment later they were all seated around the kitchen table, playing brag with enthusiasm, Grandie notching their scores with matchsticks in a battered old wooden scoring board.

Marina said nothing to either of the two men, but she looked from one to the other curiously. It was yet another instance of the secret between them. Gideon had known before he reached up to the shelf that the cards were kept there. He had known that Grandie's favourite game was brag. Marina and Grandie had spent many nights playing cards in this kitchen. When she was a little girl, Grandie would exchange sweets for the points she had taken in their games. If he won outright she would owe him time, time he expected her to spend in practicing.

How had Gideon known that? Unless the roots of his acquaintance with Grandie went back a long, long way, and if they did why had Marina never set eyes on him in her life before?

CHAPTER TWO

MARINA went to bed at ten as usual. The floors of
the old house creaked noisily, the boards having
shrunk and warped a good deal. On windy nights
she often thought they sounded like complaining
little voices. Tonight, though, she heard other voices
—those of Grandie and Gideon downstairs in the
kitchen. They had closed the door, but the sound
came up through the low ceiling. She could not
make out the words, but the tones were sharp and
hostile. Grandie was arguing with their guest. Once
or twice his voice sounded quite furious. Gideon
answered quietly, softly, but with an unshakeable
determination.

'What does it mean?' Marina asked Meg and
Emma. They sat in their accustomed places on the
end of her bed, one against each wooden post. Meg
was very small and very neat, with tidy black curls
visible beneath her yellow velvet bonnet, small
black shoes just below the hem of her matching
velvet coat. She had been Edwardian, the doll belonging to Grandie's sister Aunt Meg, who had died
aged twelve. Marina thought of Meg as her cousin.
During her rather isolated childhood she had invented this family for herself. The two dolls made it

possible for her to have conversations. Emma was younger but larger, a floppy great rag doll with enormous sewn-on blue eyes and green ballet shoes tied on her feet. She had belonged to Marina's mother, Grandie said. He had never bought Marina a new doll and she would not have wanted one. These two were more than enough for her.

They had been with her for so many years. She would not want to part with either of them. Looking at them now, kneeling on her bed in her brief white cotton nightie, she waited for their reply and got none at all.

'You're useless, do you know that?'

She climbed into bed. 'All the same, something funny is going on, I'm sure of that. Do you think Gideon knows a dark secret from Grandie's former life?' Her eyes widened. 'Maybe Gideon is Grandie's illegitimate son by a Russian ballet dancer or a French opera singer.'

Meg's small face held ineffable contempt. Marina eyed her. 'No, maybe you're right,' she sighed. 'Romantic but unlikely. Grandmama would never have allowed it.' She had no real knowledge of her grandmother, but the large yellowed photograph of her in the parlour showed a lady with a forthright chin and speaking eyes. Marina could not imagine Grandie daring to be unfaithful to her.

Grandmama had died thirty years ago. Marina's father had been a young man of twenty, but there were no photographs of him downstairs. Grandie was always elusive about him, brushing aside her questions. She screwed up her nose. Hadn't there once been a picture somewhere? She thought she remembered one, but she could not be sure and it had certainly now gone.

Marina had a suspicion that her father had been rather wicked. In some way he had offended Grandie. She knew that her grandfather was very secretive about his past and the icy look which could invade his eyes was always enough to deter her from asking too many questions.

Curling up, her cheek on her hand, she slowly slid into sleep and when she woke up the daylight was streaming into the room. For a moment she lay there, yawning, then she uncoiled, stretching, and said good morning to Meg and Emma. Washed and dressed, she made her bed and went down the stairs. Grandie had lately begun to stay in bed in the morning. He was seventy-one and was beginning to conserve what was left of his life force.

It surprised her to walk into the kitchen and hear the kettle singing away. Gideon turned with a smile and Marina grinned back at him.

'You're up early!'

'It seemed a pity to waste such a day lying in bed.'

She looked out of the low window. Gideon had drawn the red check curtains and sunlight streamed into the room. The dew was still sparkling on grass and flowers, the vivid crimson roses unfolding on the trellis, the scarlet of poppies trembling heavy-headed, white lilac clustered just behind them. A mistle-thrush sat on the lilac tree, turning his little glistening black eye to inspect the lawn for signs of insects. The sky above him was a brilliant blue.

'It is a lovely day,' she agreed.

'A day for a picnic,' said Gideon, spooning tea into the pot.

Marina's eyes opened wide. 'A picnic?'

'We could walk up to the grave circle,' Gideon suggested.

Staring at him, she asked, 'How do you know about that?'

He shot her a look. 'The finest grave circle in the north-west? It's in all the guide-books.'

'Oh,' she said. Was it? She had known it all her life and took it for granted but perhaps it was famous outside this area. She wouldn't know.

'It's a stiff climb up there,' she warned.

Gideon's eyes mocked. 'You think I look too decayed to make it?'

'I thought I ought to warn you,' she said, a dimple at the side of her mouth. 'What would you like for breakfast? I'm going to have a boiled egg.'

'I'll have one too,' he agreed. 'And put some others in for us to take with us on the picnic.'

When they had eaten their breakfast they searched the larder and the small refrigerator for provisions. They found some cold chicken, some salad and some fruit, and Marina searched for some digestive biscuits which they could eat with the large piece of cheese they had found.

'I'll go up and tell Grandie,' she said.

'I told him last night,' Gideon returned coolly, his hand detaining her as she was about to fly off to her grandfather.

She looked up at him in surprise. 'Oh. He didn't mind?' Was that what they had been arguing about?

'He agreed that we could go,' Gideon said unrevealingly.

They packed all their food in an old wicker

basket which they carried between them. They had to pass through the village to reach the field from which one climbed to the top of Circle Hill. Mrs Robinson peered from the Post Office window, framed on each side by a black cat. She stared curiously at Gideon and waved to Marina. 'We'll have to say hello,' she told him resignedly. 'She'll be hurt if we don't.'

Mrs Robinson lurked in her shop like a spider waiting for a passing fly, but she was so sweet that it was hard to get annoyed with her. She saw every single thing that happened in the street. Marina sometimes suspected her of concealing secret radar equipment about her small, fluffy person. She seemed to ferret out every piece of information about everyone in the village. It was a small village of around a hundred people and Mrs Robinson knew them all intimately.

Grandie said her eager interest in the lives of everyone round her kept her preserved. She fixed one with that bright, happy smile and the soft gentle voice asked questions unblushingly. Her only grandchild had emigrated to Australia—to get away from Mrs Robinson, it was rumoured. But the old lady was always cheerful, despite her empty private life. Her mission in life engrossed her to the fullest. She was an information service. She gathered it and she passed it on, often, Grandie said, much embellished. Mrs Robinson was an artist. She was not content with life as it was—she improved upon it.

As Marina and Gideon walked into the little shop she came gaily forward, already talking. 'I expect you're going for a nice picnic. Just the day for it.

What a very nice car your friend has got! Staying with you and Mr Grandison, is he? That's nice for you. Mrs Bellish had her baby on Tuesday. Bald, it was, bald as an egg. Poor Mr Bellish, he was shaken—well, it was the first. It just shows, doesn't it? The cat at Ivy Tree got stuck up the chimney. I told her it would. Shot up there every time anyone went into the room. You can't take in a wild creature, I said. A wild cat is a wild cat, it won't change.'

'A bottle of lemonade, please,' said Marina when she paused for breath, making no attempt to answer or ask any questions, since it was quite unnecessary. Mrs Robinson would go her own way regardless.

Reaching down the bottle, Mrs Robinson fixed Gideon with a smile. 'Come from London, have you?' She did not wait for an answer. Grandie said she read the replies in people's faces and if she didn't like them she made up her own. 'Never been there, I haven't. Nasty place, full of fog. Mr Robinson took me to Blackpool once, but never again. I was so tired getting there and back I needed a holiday when I got home again. Anything else, was it, Marina? How's Mr Grandison's hands? Getting bad, aren't they? Nearly crippled, poor man. Nettles, that's the thing he needs. Mr Robinson swore by them.' A small boy came wandering in and started poring over the boxes of penny sweets arranged at the front of the counter. Mrs Robinson switched her gaze to him and Marina put down the right money on the counter.

'Good morning, Mrs Robinson,' she said.

Gideon followed her from the shop, laughing

under his breath. They heard the old lady talking
to the little boy and getting the same silence from
him.

'Incredible, isn't she?' said Gideon.

They turned through the gate, carefully closing
it after them, and began to walk through the long
bearded grass, feeling it whisper against their legs.
A great mass of buttercups grew among it and some
black and white cows came heavily down from the
top to inspect them.

'Curious creatures, cows,' Gideon observed as
they lowered their heads to low mournfully at them.

If Gideon had ever been a regular visitor to the
village, Mrs Robinson would have recognised him,
Marina thought, but she had shown no sign of
recognition just now. Her little eyes had glinted
beadily over him, taking in the casual dark blue
denims he wore, the open-necked blue shirt and
wide leather belt which emphasised his slim waist.

Marina was wearing a tight-waisted green cotton
dress with shirring at the bodice, her small breasts
lifting beneath the thin material, giving her a graceful outline. The full skirt blew out as she walked with
the wind behind her.

They climbed the stile at the top of the field.
Gideon went first and put down the basket, then
turned to lift Marina down. His hands tightened
on her waist for a moment as he set her down, then
dropped away and he turned to pick up the basket.

The grave circle lay on the very crest of the hill,
overlooking the valleys on all sides. It was almost
four thousand years old and had been in use during
the bronze age.

'These are probably the graves of kings,' said Marina, standing in the centre of the broken grey stones. 'There are half a dozen of them, a whole dynasty, buried up here to keep an eye on their subjects after death, presumably.'

'Big brother is watching you,' Gideon offered.

She giggled. 'Something like that. Creepy, isn't it? I used to look up at the hill when I was little and believe that at night they came out of their graves and went stealing down the hill in search of victims.'

'This must have been an enormous chap,' Gideon murmured, standing at the opening to one grave. Stones had been erected on four sides of it. Oblong, raised, covered in grass, it was over six foot long. Gideon lay down inside the wall of stones, his hands crossed across his chest.

'Don't!' Marina cried in dismay. 'It's unlucky!'

Gideon looked up at her, grinning. He looked, she thought, as if he might have been one of them, those far-off barbarian kings, with a long Celtic face, all harsh bones and lantern jaw, the black hair wild and windblown, the eyes glinting dangerously through those black eyelashes. All he needed was a horned helmet and a sword.

She told him her view and he laughed at her. 'You've got your periods all muddled up. It was the Vikings who wore horned helmets and the Celts who had long faces. I think the earlier chaps who built these graves must have been rather short fellows. Most of them are just five foot. This one is exceptional.'

'Please get out of it,' she begged, not liking to see

him lying on that sheep-cropped turf.

She picked up the basket and left the circle of graves. Up here the wind blew fiercely and if she looked up the sky seemed so close one could almost touch it, moving overhead in a troubled confusion of clouds and wind. Below the valleys were green and fertile, lying trapped in sunlight like a fly in amber, with dark pools of shadow where there were trees in the sides of fields, and cows moving ponderously in a slow procession.

She found a sunwarmed hollow in the side of the hill just below the brow on the side less visited by the wind and sank down on the short turf. Gideon dropped down beside her, stretching his long legs with a sigh.

'This is nice.'

She spread out the food on the white cloth they had brought and Gideon lazily leaned over to take a leg of chicken. 'I'm hungry again,' he said.

'It's almost twelve,' she said, surprised at how rapidly the morning had gone. It had been eight when they ate their breakfast.

A lark hovered high overhead, the small wings seeming not to move at all, so that it appeared to hang there as if suspended by a string. Song poured from it and Marina lay full length to stare up at it, shielding her eyes from the sun with one hand.

The grass under her back was warm and smelt delicious. Out of the wind it was languidly hot and she half wished for the shade of one of the trees down in the valley; there was no cover up here. She peered at Gideon. He was neatly stripping the meat from his chicken, his white teeth even and efficient.

'Cannibal!' she said.

He looked at her with charm in his face, his eyes wrinkled in amusement. 'Aren't you going to eat?'

She yawned. 'Too lazy.'

He wrapped the chicken bone in a piece of paper and put it in the basket, then shifted to get some cheese and a digestive biscuit.

'Here you are, lazybones,' he said in a deep, dark brown voice at her side.

She took her hand away from her eyes and saw his black head blocking the sky above her. For a few seconds her heart raced oddly. Gideon stared down at her. She looked into the black eyes and then down at the hard, sensual mouth.

As he bent forward she knew he was going to kiss her. It was a gentle kiss, soft and exploratory, almost a question, as if Gideon were unsure.

When he drew back Marina said a little breathlessly, 'I think I've met you in another life.'

'Do you believe in reincarnation?' he asked, laughing.

'I've never thought about it, but ...'

'But what?' he asked quickly, watching her.

'Have we met before?' she asked him.

Gideon stared down at her. His face had that strange emptiness again, his black eyes bottomless, unplumbable.

'What makes you think we have?'

'Something familiar about you,' she said. 'I'm certain I've seen your face somewhere before.'

He studied her. 'I hope the impression was a favourable one.'

It was an odd thing for him to say and she felt

that he was waiting almost with anxiety for her to reply.

'I don't feel like running away shrieking whenever I see you,' she told him lightly.

'What do you feel like?'

Again that hard ring of question in his voice. Marina frowned, staring at him.

'Why won't you tell me? There's something, isn't there? You and Grandie are hiding something from me.'

He drew back then, smiling drily. 'What a vivid imagination you've got! Eat your cheese.' He proffered it again and she slowly took it, aware that he was avoiding any further discussion.

'What sort of businessman are you?' she asked him.

'The busy sort,' he said coolly. 'I've been working flat out for months. I'm mentally and physically exhausted.'

She considered him, nibbling her cheese. 'You look as if you're more at home in luxury hotels than little cottages.'

He grimaced. 'I see enough of hotels in the rest of the year. I travel widely and one can get very tired of hotel life.'

Marina sighed. 'Oh, I'd love to get tired of it.'

There was a curious silence. Gideon stared at the valley, his face rigid, the harsh bone structure dominant, making his features seem fleshless like an eagle's hooked profile, the black hair blown back off his high forehead.

He raked a hand through it and she watched. 'You have a good span,' she told him suddenly. 'Do you play the piano?'

His mouth twisted. 'Slightly,' he said.

'You must play to me when we get back,' she said, delighted.

'I'd rather not,' Gideon said flatly. 'I'm not in your class.'

She seized one of his hands and laid it over her palm, surveying the sinewy length of it, studying the strong fingers.

'It's a powerful hand.'

'What are you? A palmist?' he asked derisively.

She began to laugh and turned his hand over to view the palm. It was smooth and pale, the lines bitten into it deeply. 'A good life line,' she told him. 'But very little heart line. On the other hand your head line is extra strong.'

He chuckled. 'Clever stuff! You forgot to ask me to cross your palm with silver.'

'All contributions received gratefully,' she retorted with a smile.

He drew a fifty-pence piece out of his pocket and laid it on her hand.

'Thank you, little gypsy.'

She bit it. 'Not over-generous, but it will do. Thank you.' She slipped the coin into her pocket. 'I'll buy a new crystal ball.'

'Too late,' he mocked. 'You've already met the dark stranger.'

She looked at him through her lashes. 'But are you a stranger?'

He stared at the impudent curve of her cheek, the slight smile on her small pink mouth. 'Yes,' he whispered. 'Am I?'

The crunch of grass disturbed their concentration on each other. They started, looking round, and the mild surprised eyes of a sheep gazed at them from the top of the hill. They laughed and the sheep skipped away in dismay.

Gideon stretched out again and ate some more of the food, lying on his side, watching the shadows chasing across the grass lower down the hill.

Marina ate a little salad and an apple. Her face was flushed with sun now and she felt sleepily disinclined to move. A hooded crow flew down and watched them avidly, stalking to and fro like Hamlet on the battlements of Elsinore, waiting for the crumbs of their food. Gideon had laid out the chicken on a paper napkin. Suddenly the crow leapt forward and grabbed a piece of chicken, flapping away with it in its beak.

They both burst into laughter. 'Do you think he'll eat it?' asked Marina, and Gideon nodded.

'Crows are flesh-eaters.'

'Ugh, how horrid!'

'They steal fledglings from nests, didn't you know?'

'I suppose I did. I just never thought about it. I know butterflies eat carrion because Grandie told me long ago. I was disgusted. They look so pure and ethereal, yet they feed on putrid flesh.' She shuddered. 'It makes one see them in quite a different light.'

'Life's more complicated than it seems,' Gideon agreed.

He lay on his back, his hands locked behind his head, and stared at the sky. Marina saw his eyes close and the harsh features smooth out into peace. The lines of his mouth softened and grew gentle.

The bones relaxed from whatever tension was holding them. At ease like this, Gideon looked a gentle, tender man, his mouth curved warmly, the glitter of the clever black eyes hidden under those heavy lids. His lashes lay in a black arc across his cheeks.

She let him sleep, unwilling to disturb him. Some more sheep appeared to crop noisily on the short turf above them. A few gulls swooped in the blue sky above the village, their wings white curves against the sky. The sea glittered in the sunlight, dancing blue waves receding into a haze which hovered some way off shore towards the horizon.

Gideon snorted and she saw his lids flicker. Bending, she watched consciousness come back into his face. He opened his eyes and looked up at her. She smiled at him, the limp fine drift of her silver-white hair drooping towards him.

He put a lazy hand to it. 'Moonlight,' he said deeply.

'You slept very deeply.'

He frowned. 'How rude! I'm sorry.'

'Don't apologise. I didn't mind—I had company.'

He raised his brows.

Marina glanced at the sheep and down at the gulls. 'There's always plenty of company around if you look for it.'

He smiled again, his mouth tender. 'Like Emma and Meg?'

Marina's eyes opened wide, their blue gleam vivid. 'How do you know about them?'

'Your grandfather told me,' he said, but there had been a brief pause before he spoke and she wondered if she was imagining all these odd little glances, strange little silences. He had said she had a vivid imagination, but Marina wondered.

She glanced at the sky. 'I think we should start going down. Grandie will wonder where we've got to.'

She rose and he extended a lazy hand. Laughing, she pulled on it and he rose to her side. Still holding her hand, he looked down at her. 'You're pink. You've caught the sun.'

'My skin!' she moaned. 'I can't be out in the sun for a moment without turning lobster red.'

'Not lobster today,' he assured her. 'More of a salmon pink.'

She laughed. 'Oh, thanks. You're very reassuring.'

'I adore salmon,' he said, and kissed her cheek.

They walked down the hill much faster than they had gone up, but it still took them half an hour to cover the distance to the village. As they passed the post office Mrs Robinson came hurrying out with Grandie's newspaper. Marina smiled and listened to the spilling sentences. When it was possible to move without being rude she smiled again and said they must go.

Walking towards the cottage, Gideon said with amusement, 'What does anyone need a newspaper for around here? Mrs Robinson does it for nothing.'

'They don't put the really interesting news in newspapers,' Marina said. 'When Mrs Dudeck locked her husband in the coal cellar for the night it never got published in the newspaper, but we all knew about it. And what newspaper would print the fact that the third Smith baby wasn't Mr Smith's but the milkman's?'

'Good heavens!' said Gideon, laughing loudly. 'How on earth did she know that?'

'Heaven knows. Guesswork or sheer invention or the fact that the poor baby has got ginger hair and so has the milkman.'

'For a quiet little community you seem to have a lot of scandal.'

'The quieter the community the more the scandal,' Marina told him gravely. 'Grandie firmly believes she makes it all up, but I'm not so sure.'

Gideon moved silently beside her as they entered the cottage. 'Does she invent anything about Grandie?'

Marina turned her head quickly to look at him. 'What?' she asked.

Gideon's face was unreadable. 'God knows. You tell me.'

Marina frowned. 'I've never heard her say anything, but then that isn't the way she operates. She tells you everything about everyone else, but she never lets on what she knows about you.'

Gideon began to whistle softly under his breath. Grandie looked up as they entered the kitchen, his face tense and frowning. Marina kissed him lightly, hoping he wasn't going to be cross. He stared at her for a few seconds with intent probing, but then he smiled.

'You look as if you've had a warm climb.'

'It was fun,' she said. 'We lost some of our picnic to a horrid old crow, but Gideon ate the rest.'

'You had some salad and an apple,' Gideon protested, his black eyes teasing.

'Big deal.' She looked at the bubbling saucepan Grandie was stirring. 'Stew?'

He nodded. 'Lamb,' he told her.

'Do you like lamb stew, Gideon?' she asked.

'Love it,' said Gideon. He handed Grandie the paper and Grandie sat down with it at the table. Marina walked to the door.

'I think I'll change and have a wash.'

Grandie was staring at the newspaper and didn't answer. Gideon smiled at her, his eyes on her face.

'You've got smut on your nose,' he told her as if it delighted him.

She made a face at him and went out. Glancing back as she closed the door, she caught sight of Grandie's face. He was still staring at the newspaper and he looked pale.

She washed and changed into a pale pink linen dress with a stiff round collar. When she got down to the kitchen the two men were talking quietly. They looked round and stopped speaking as soon as she entered the room.

Marina sat down and looked around for the paper. 'Where's the paper, Grandie? I want to read my stars. What's your birth month, Gideon? You look like an Arian.'

'Good lord,' he said, mocking her.

She opened her eyes. 'You aren't?'

'No,' he said, 'I'm not.'

They laughed as their eyes met.

'Don't tease,' she said. 'What are you?'

'A man who doesn't believe in a word of it,' he retorted.

'Where's the paper?' she asked.

Grandie glanced at Gideon with a hesitant face.

'I'm sorry,' said Gideon, grimacing. 'It's my fault,

I wrapped the remains of our picnic in it and flung it into the range.'

Marina looked into the impassive black eyes and she knew that he was lying.

Grandie went to the saucepan and took off the lid. A savoury steam rose into the air. 'Nearly ready,' he said. 'Are you hungry, Gideon?'

'Ravenous. I'll lay the table,' said Gideon. 'If you don't mind moving, my lady.' He bent over her chair and his cheek brushed hers. The black eyes smiled at her and Marina found herself smiling back, but with a reluctance she could not explain. She liked Gideon. He was very attractive, he could be very charming, but he was a liar and she could not fathom what was going on at all, only that whatever it was, it was putting shadows under Grandie's tired old eyes and lines around his mouth, and somehow that look had only been there since Gideon arrived.

CHAPTER THREE

WHEN she woke up next morning the sun was streaming across the walls and she heard a blackbird somewhere in the garden telling the world that morning had broken. Leaping out of bed, she pattered on bare feet to the window and leaned on the sill, taking deep breaths of sea air, then glanced down at a movement and saw Gideon with his hands on his lean hips and the wind ruffling his black hair. At that instant he seemed to sense her presence and glanced up. She smiled and got a crooked smile back, his eyes warm.

'Come down, lazybones,' he called. 'I'm waiting for you.'

She felt no urge to hurry. Propping up her chin with her elbows on the sill, she threw back, 'It's too lovely a day to waste in rushing about. I'm going to take my time.'

'Come down or I'll come and get you,' he said softly, almost as though he were enjoying making the threat.

For a second she thought of challenging him to do just that. The glint in his eyes told her he knew what she was thinking. They observed each other, smiling, and he moved slightly, poised to come into the house and carry out his threat. Marina laughed. 'I'm coming,' she said, backing down.

'Wise of you,' Gideon advised her gently, grinning.

She moved away from the window and stood with her arms curved over her head, standing on her tiptoes, smiling. She felt as though her veins ran with new life. She wanted to burst into song. It was such a lovely morning, the world had been reborn. Marina was reluctant to move even now, cherishing the happiness which she had discovered inside herself.

When she did come down she found the table laid for breakfast and the fragrance of coffee in the air mingling with the smell of bacon. Gideon turned and slid the dark eyes down her. He didn't say a word, but she knew he approved the thin yellow cotton dress with a pleated skirt and demure scalloped collar. She walked forward and was going to sit down when he touched her bare arm gently. She turned to look at him in enquiry and his mouth grazed across her cheek and was gone. He moved to get the breakfast from the oven where it was keeping warm. Marina, very flushed, sat down. She was not surprised by the soft kiss, but one part of her mind warned her that she should not let him take it for granted that he could kiss her when he liked.

She had only known him for a day. It was a very short acquaintance. Her thoughts were confused because the brevity of their friendship seemed to have no bearing on the way they felt and acted. This puzzling familiarity persisted. Common sense seemed to have nothing to do with it.

'I thought we'd go for a drive,' Gideon said as he drank his coffee later.

'Where to?' She was excited at once. She had rarely driven in a car. She thought of the small yellow sports car and her face flushed with anticipation.

He shrugged. 'Does it matter? We'll just drive and see where we get to, shall we?'

She glanced at the door and he caught that look and smiled at her. 'Grandie won't mind.'

Sometimes he called her grandfather Mr Grandison quite formally as though he barely knew him. Other times he used the familiar nickname and she caught the echo of a casual familiarity. A small line etched itself between her brows, giving her smooth young face a troubled look, and Gideon gave her a quick, penetrating stare.

'Something wrong? You don't want to come?' He sounded curt and she responded involuntarily.

'Of course I do.' She smiled. 'I'd love to come.'

Gideon took quiet byroads out of the usual rapid rush of the traffic along the coast, avoiding towns and main roads, his speed keeping to a regular pace which gave them a chance to view the countryside. Marina got the distinct impression that he knew this coast extremely well. He seemed to know all these short cuts, weaving in and out of main roads, crossing them and returning to the timeless peace of the deserted countryside again without consulting any maps.

Glancing at his watch, he said: 'I thought we'd lunch at a pub. You won't mind a scratch meal? I know somewhere quiet where they do a bar meal— sandwiches, sausages, that sort of thing.'

'It sounds fine,' she agreed.

They had not spoken much as they drove. Marina had been content with the wind rushing through her hair and the scent of the fields on either side. Glancing at him, she wondered if he were silent by nature or if he just had nothing to say to her. He seemed to enjoy being with her. Every now and then he looked sideways at her and his face had a smile on it which warmed her, yet he seemed to avoid conversation, keeping it on that impersonal level, rarely speaking of anything about himself.

It occurred to her that he might be in some sort

of trouble. Was he hiding down here? And from what? Gideon did not look the sort of man who ran from things, but in relaxation she sometimes caught a grimness in his face, a hint of tension which she could not fathom.

'How long are you going to stay?' she asked suddenly as they drew into a small gravelled car park, and Gideon's hands jerked on the wheel.

She heard the screech of the tires as he righted the steering and parked. He sat staring at the hedge in front of which the car had come to rest.

'I haven't made up my mind. It all depends.'

'On what?'

He turned the black head and his eyes scrutinised her face as though he searched her own eyes for some expression. 'On a number of things,' he said slowly, and she sensed that whatever he had looked for in her eyes, he had not found. What had he looked for?

She wanted to ask if he were in trouble, but he looked suddenly aloof and she did not quite dare. He got out of the car and came round to help her from her seat.

The bar was small and highly polished and almost empty. An old man in a flat cap sat reading a newspaper in a corner and a pair of young people whispered together at a table. The barman served them with sandwiches and hot sausages. Gideon had lager and Marina had a tall glass of lemonade with a slice of lemon floating in it and ice clinking around against the glass as she carried it.

There were ornate Edwardian mirrors on the walls and when she looked up at them she was sure she had seen them before. Her brow creased. Had Grandie brought her here? she wondered. Gideon saw her frown and asked quietly: 'What's wrong?'

'Those mirrors,' she said. 'They look familiar.'

He glanced at them, shrugged. 'You see them in a lot of old pubs. Some London theatres, too. They were very popular at one time.'

'Do you like the theatre?' she asked him. 'I've been a few times. Grandie takes me. We go by train and stay the night in London.' It had always been an exciting journey. Marina often felt sick with eagerness the night before. Her face reflected that excitement now, her eyes wide and brilliant, and Gideon watched her with narrowed inspection, reading the quiver of her pink mouth, the little coins of red in her cheeks.

'You're too highly strung,' he said flatly, and she bit her lower lip, admitting it.

She had always been volatile, responsive to feeling and circumstance. Grandie said it was one of her gifts, it was what made her music so charged, but it was also one of her curses because she could not control the depth of emotion which could take hold of her.

After they had finished their meal and the drinks, they drove off again and skirted the suburban sprawl of a large town. The car slowed as traffic engulfed it and Gideon grimaced at her.

'It will take us a time to get through this,' he apologised.

She leaned her elbow on the back of the seat between them, smiling at him. 'I don't mind.' She was too happy to mind anything. Her eyes lingered on the hard face and Gideon leaned slowly over to kiss her lightly on the mouth.

As he drew away Marina became conscious of being watched. She looked up, flushed after Gideon's kiss, and saw a long sleek red car just behind them. It was being driven by a short balding man, but it was not him who was staring. It was the woman beside him, and although Marina could not quite see her face she was aware that there was hostility in the way the eyes behind the dark sunglasses were watching her.

Gideon sensed her glancing back and turned his black head. Marina felt the shock run through him. She sat up, staring at him, and Gideon turned to look back at her again. He was white. Marina was not imagining anything this time: Gideon had gone white from the black line of his hair to his straight, tense mouth.

A horn blared. Gideon looked round again and Marina saw the woman wave her hand in an imperious, compelling fashion. At the same moment the red car drew into the curb and stopped. Gideon stared ahead at the road. His hands gripped the wheel and Marina saw his knuckles pale at the pressure he was exerting. His face was averted from her, but there was no mistaking the way his black brows knit and the muscle jerking in his flat brown cheek.

She could sense that he was turning over a course of action in his mind. The horn blared again and Marina looked quickly at him. 'They want you to stop,' she pointed out. 'They know you, don't they?'

Gideon did not answer. He spun the car into the

curb and parked some way ahead of the other car, then he opened his door and slid his legs out. Turning his head, he looked at Marina, his face implacable. 'Stay in the car,' he ordered in a harsh voice.

She opened her mouth and he said it again, even more sharply. 'Stay in the car!'

He walked away very fast, his long lean body stiff and erect. Marina would not look now. She was wounded at the way he had spoken to her, the cold light in the dark eyes. She sat facing the road, but her eyes would not keep away from the driving mirror. In it she saw the woman leave the red car, her movements graceful as she walked round to meet Gideon. She had black hair, as black as his, but brushed sleekly into a high chignon on the back of her head. Marina could not see her face as she walked. The enormous sunglasses hid her eyes, but her mouth was a glossy red and it curved into a smile as she and Gideon met on the pavement.

Marina could not hear what they said, but there was no need for her to hear. She saw the woman fling her arms around Gideon, her hands clasp his face and pull his head down. As their lips met, Marina made herself look away because she was so angry she wanted to leap out of the car and walk away. She was innocent about men, but she was not a child. She recognised the eager sensuality of the woman's body as she kissed Gideon.

She would not look at them again. She laced her fingers together and studied them, waiting for Gideon to come back. The clock on the dashboard ticked and she heard every soft sound it made. Time passed like something with leaden feet. Whatever the woman and Gideon were saying to each other, it was taking a long time. She could not bear it at last. She had to look. They still stood there, the woman talking, her face lifted to his, her hand on his arm, the fingers pressing into him possessively.

Gideon's face was stiff and cold: Marina could see that from this distance. She probed his features, trying to read the feelings behind that hard expression, but whatever they were Gideon was obviously merely waiting for the woman to finish what she was saying. His whole attitude spoke of restless impatience, a desire to go.

Suddenly the woman hit him. Marina sat up, stiffening, feeling as though the blow had been at herself.

Gideon moved sharply in reaction. For a second his hand was raised as though he were going to hit the woman back. He bit out something with his mouth moving fiercely, barely parted, the words pushed through his taut lips.

Then he turned on his heel and walked away. Marina looked back down at her linked hands. Gideon climbed into the driving seat and as he did so Marina distinctly heard running feet on the pavement. She looked up and Gideon started the car. The woman was coming towards them, her racing feet clicking on the paving stones. The car slid out into the traffic and she halted, hands clenched at her sides.

Marina picked up the emotions eating her and shivered. They were not all directed at Gideon. Some of that bitter feeling was aimed at her, and she shuddered away from it, looking away.

Gideon drove without speaking, his face in profile, as sharp as a newly minted coin, his jaw and cheekbones locked tight in rage. Marina stared out of the window and knew he would not tell her what that had all been about. A silence hung between them like a veil through which she saw darkly.

Marina could guess at some of it. It had been very obvious, even to her inexperience, that the woman was in love with Gideon, that at some time in the past there had been a relationship between them, and the way the woman had pressed herself against him as she kissed him, warned that the relationship had been intimate. Gideon's coldness, hardness, suggested that there had been some sort of quarrel and that although the woman still cared for him Gideon was angry with her. Just angry? Marina pondered, remembering the look on his face, the white shock, when he saw the woman at first.

Whatever was or had been between them, it had left a residue in Gideon which marked his face now with anger and some harsh emotion. Jealousy? she thought. Had the other woman been unfaithful to him? Did that explain the brooding darkness in his face as he drove?

Although Marina had not been able to see much of her face, she had picked up beauty in the movements of the body, the shape of the mouth and the confident, alluring smile she had given Gideon as she kissed him.

Gideon was not a boy. He was a man who was almost twice Marina's age and obviously he must have had affairs in the past. It was none of Marina's business and she was angry with herself for sitting here with a heart like lead and a sense of depression. She had only known him for two short days. What business was it of hers? He had told her nothing of his past life and she had no right to care that that woman had kissed him so passionately.

She concentrated on the hedges swishing past. They were back in the quiet countryside and she guessed they were headed for Basslea again. Gideon had not spoken for so long that when he did speak she jumped and looked round at him, startled, her eyes wide.

'I'm sorry I spoke sharply just now,' he said, his dark eyes probing hers.

She looked away. 'It doesn't matter.'

'It does,' he said harshly.

She shrugged. 'I realised you were upset about meeting your friend.'

He laughed shortly. 'She's no friend of mine.'

Marina did not respond to that, although her heart lifted a little at the anger in his voice.

'She seemed very disturbed,' she offered, aware that she was trying to get him to talk about it and ashamed of her curiosity but unable to stop herself.

Gideon didn't answer, though. He drove with his eyes intent on the road ahead and the dark anger was visible in his face again. After a moment, he said, 'I'm sorry I spoke to you like that, though.'

It was her turn not to answer. She was suddenly invaded by anger, guessing that he was patronising her, regretting that he had spoken to her in anger because ever since they met he had been very careful of her. He had treated her like a child and he was treating her like one now.

She knew that he was watching her obliquely and she turned her head away because she did not want him to know that she resented his attitude to her.

The rest of the drive was accomplished in silence. As he stopped the car, he turned and put a hand over hers. 'Are you angry with me?' His tone pleaded gently and she had to look at him.

'Of course not,' she said politely. 'Why should I be?'

'I can't explain,' he broke out roughly. 'Will you forgive me for speaking to you like that?'

'I said I did,' Marina reminded quietly, and pulled her hand out from under his before she got out of the car.

She did not turn towards the cottage. She moved away towards the cliff and Gideon came after her in his long stride, catching her arm.

'Where are you going?' There was that odd hoarse anxiety in his voice and she saw sweat on his forehead.

Frowning, puzzled, she said, 'For a walk.'

'We should get back to Grandie,' Gideon told her, his hand tightening round her arm.

'You go,' said Marina in an uneven voice. 'I want to walk.'

As she turned he came with her and she looked at him levelly. 'Alone, please,' she told him without anger or rudeness. 'I like walking alone.'

She walked away and Gideon stood there watching her for a long time. She went down the cliff path and heard the free shriek of the gulls on the warm air, their soaring swooping flight all round her. The sea lay glittering at her feet and the turf had a sundrenched sweetness which filled her nostrils. She lay down and breathed quietly. For some reason she had felt claustrophobic on the way back in the car. She had wanted—no, she had needed, to get away from Gideon. Something in him oppressed her. She could not put her finger on what it was—an emotion, a pressure within him of which she was ignorant but of which she could not be unaware. Although she did not know what it was, she did know she had to get away from it. It was a pressure on her, too, and the fact that she did not understand what it was made the pressure greater.

She heard a stone rattle past and the slither of feet. Gideon? She tensed, turning her head, but it was not him. It was a young man in a striped T-shirt and jeans with binoculars round his neck. The sun had caught his skin, turning him a rough pink, and his short fair hair prickled across his forehead, perspiration making it clear he had been walking for a long time.

He paused, seeing her. 'Oh!' The exclamation was surprised and not displeased. He smiled. 'Sorry if I'm disturbing you.'

'You're not.' Marina half moved to get up and he sat down beside her, his eyes on her.

'Don't go. Please. I'd hate to think I've driven you away.'

She half laughed. 'You haven't. I was just going.'

'Not yet,' he pleaded, his hand on her arm. 'Tell me, how far is it to the nearest village?'

She sat down again, her arms propping her up. 'Basslea is a short walk from here.'

He got out a map from the rucksack on his back and she pointed it out to him, their heads close together. 'Would you like a drink?' He produced a plastic bottle of orange squash from the clustered contents of the rucksack and then a small plastic mug. They each drank a little. The young man extended his hand after packing the bottle and mug away again.

'I'm Tom Hutton.'

Marina told him her name and saw his face reflect interest and surprise. 'What a gorgeous name! And apt.' He glanced at the sea and sighed. 'Are you on holiday too?'

'I live here.'

'Even more apt, then,' he agreed. 'I'm on holiday, a walking tour. I work in Birmingham all through the year and it's heavenly to get out of the place.'

'What sort of work?' she asked.

'I'm a draughtsman. It's work that needs a lot of concentration and it can be deadly dull.' He stared at her hair, blowing in the faint sea breeze. 'What fantastic hair you've got! I don't think I've ever seen hair that colour before. Is it genuine?'

Marina laughed. 'You suspect I've dyed it? No, it's mine all right. It was even lighter when I was little.'

'That must be impossible,' said Tom Hutton, fingering a strand of it. 'I can't imagine it.'

A sound behind them made them both turn. Gideon stood on the edge of the cliff with his black

eyes fixed on them and a harsh frown running between his brows.

'Marina!' he spoke tersely. 'Your grandfather
wants you.'

Tom's hand dropped away from her hair and
she turned to smile at him. 'It was nice to meet
you.'

'Maybe we'll bump into each other again,' he
said with a hopeful inflection. 'I might stay in the
village for a few days. I want to take a look at these
birds.' He indicated his binoculars.

'You're a birdwatcher?' She laughed, sym-
pathetically. 'Not much chance of that in Birmingham, I suppose.'

'Marina!' Gideon's voice had a biting sound. 'Are
you coming?'

She rose, slightly flushed, and Tom glanced
round at Gideon with a faintly irritated expression.
'Is that your father?'

Marina laughed and then stopped laughing as
she felt Gideon's rage coming towards them. He had
heard the question and he was not pleased.

'No,' she said, and started to walk back up the
cliff. 'Goodbye, Tom.'

'See you later,' said Tom.

As she reached the cliff top Gideon's arm shot
out and jerked her on to the path. She sensed that
he was in a black temper. There was violence in
him and although he did not do so she suspected
that he would like to shake her. All the tenderness
and gentleness had gone from his face. This was
another man, a cold hard man with eyes which held
no warmth.

'How did you pick him up?' he demanded.

'He's on a walking tour and he's going to stay in the village.' She turned her head to look at him, frowning. 'Why?'

'You shouldn't talk to strangers. You don't know anything about him.'

'I don't know anything about you,' she pointed our. 'You're a stranger.' In many ways he was far more of a stranger than Tom Hutton, whose kind honesty lay written in his flushed, fair face. Tom was a straightforward young man; one only had to look at him to see that. He did not have Gideon Firth's complexity or dark side.

'You know what I mean,' he brushed aside with an irritable shrug.

'No,' she contradicted, 'I don't.' She had thought she knew him by now, but that incident when he spoke with such cold ferocity to the woman with sunglasses had altered her whole view of him. She did not know the reasons for it, but she did know this—the woman had been distressed and emotional and Gideon had treated her with icy indifference. Marina found that disturbing.

Gideon halted and turned towards her, his face tense. 'I wouldn't hurt you, Marina, but you can't be sure about other people.'

'Tom wouldn't hurt anybody.' She knew that even after five minutes with him. It had been written in his open friendly face.

Gideon drew a strange, impeded breath. 'You can't be certain of that. Stay away from him. I didn't like the way he looked at you.'

Her eyes rounded in disbelief and surprise. 'What on earth do you mean?' Tom? she thought.

What nonsense! Gideon is talking nonsense.

Gideon seemed lost for words. He was frowning, his mouth straight, his jaw stiff, and she could feel a turmoil inside him, as though he were searching for a way of saying whatever it was he wanted to say, and not finding it. The frustration and impatience came out in what he did say which was curt and irrelevant. 'What did he mean—was I your father? For God's sake, do I look as if I've got a child your age?'

Marina laughed because his fury was out of proportion, it amused and softened her towards him because it indicated such vulnerability, a personal sense of insult.

'Poor Gideon!'

He caught the teasing amusement in her voice and swung towards her with a glint in the dark eyes.

'Don't laugh at me, damn you!'

'I'm sorry.' She couldn't help it, he looked so furious. Was that what had made him detest Tom on sight? Was Gideon sensitive to his age? 'I don't suppose Tom really noticed you much.'

His face changed. 'No,' he agreed. 'He was too damned busy looking at you.'

She felt herself colour and a faint quiver ran over her. Their eyes met and Gideon touched her arm, his fingertips caressing.

'Marina.' There was something in his voice which made her prickle with awareness of him. He glanced sideways along the path and then he suddenly lowered his head and kissed her hard, holding her with both hands locked on her slender shoulders, pulling her against him.

For a moment she was too surprised and shaken

by his probing kiss to be aware of anything else, then she heard the quiet tread of feet somewhere close beside them. Gideon slowly drew back his head and Marina looked past him to see Tom Hutton's fair head vanishing towards the village.

Flushed, she looked at Gideon and saw a wilful satisfaction in his face.

'You did that deliberately!' she accused.

He grinned, pleased with himself. 'Did what?'

'Why?' she demanded.

'I don't know what you mean,' said Gideon, and turned and walked towards the cottage, pulling her after him like a child, his fingers tight around her wrist.

Marina was angry with him for kissing her like that for Tom to see. She knew he had done it deliberately. He had been warning Tom off—that was too obvious to miss. But why? What right did he think he had to do such a thing?

As they entered the cottage Grandie looked round with that curious anxiety in his face and the anxiety grew as he took in Marina's hot, angry face and the way Gideon was dragging her after him.

'What's wrong?' he asked hoarsely.

'Ask him,' Marina said crossly, freeing herself with a yank of her arm.

Grandie turned his head slowly and Marina knew she was not imagining the dread in his pale face.

She looked at Gideon and caught the silent warning glittering in those black eyes as he stared at Grandie in reply.

CHAPTER FOUR

MARINA played to Gideon again after their meal. Grandie came into the room and sat in his sagging old armchair with his head back, listening, a slight frown occasionally touching his face whenever he thought she had not played a passage particularly well. Grandie was a hard taskmaster. From an early age he had made her work. 'Music is nothing but work,' he said to her. 'Work hard and let the feeling come later. Without a solid base of technique, feeling floats around uselessly. Anyone can sit and feel soulful. You have to be able to translate that emotion into sound, and to do that you must reach as near perfection as you can. Practice is the only way.'

Although Gideon was silent while she played she felt him there all the time. He sat behind her where she could not see his face without turning, yet his eyes were on her and she was aware of them.

When she had ended she turned, her hands in her lap, palms upward, her eyes flying to his face in search of response. Stranger though he was, she was eager to know how he felt about her playing. He sat looking back at her with a little smile, the black eyes brilliant. For a long moment they stared at each other. Gideon was saying nothing, yet Marina felt the warm flow of communication between them, a silent exchange which held all the response she needed.

'There was some blurring in the scherzo,' Grandie said. 'You took it too fast. I heard some slide.'

Marina turned back to the piano. 'Here,' she said wryly, and played the passage again, with a more careful attention this time, picking out the notes with clarity. Turning her head with her hair flicking in a loose silver wave, she smiled at Grandie. 'Better?'

'Better,' he said, and smiled back. He would never accept second best from her. He had never accepted it from himself. He had been a world-famous name in his profession, travelling from concert hall to concert hall around the globe, fêted and admired. That international acclaim had not meant as much to Grandie as knowing inside himself that he had performed a piece of music as he felt it was meant to be performed. For that he had worked and struggled. The by-product of fame had been irrelevant to him, although no doubt he had found it pleasant.

His son Peter had never shown any aptitude for music. 'Too lazy,' Grandie said with contempt. Marina was not sure what her father had done. Grandie was not forthcoming on that. He was a secretive man.

He got up, yawning. 'Bed,' he muttered. His hands were stiff and blue, thickly veined. Marina watched them fumble with the door handle, her heart heavy. How cruel of fate to strike at Grandie through his most precious possessions, she thought sadly.

Gideon came over to the piano and drew her to her feet. He was so much taller, the black head towering over her. She had to put back her head to look at him when they were so close and when she did she found him looking at her mouth with narrowed eyes.

In any other man she might have decided by now that he was a flirt. Now and then Marina had come up against summer visitors who imagined that a girl living alone with an old man in a remote sea-side village must be eager for experience. Marina had had no trouble in fending them off. None of them had ever attracted her in the slightest. She had learnt, though, to recognise the slightly insolent look which came before they tried to kiss her.

That was not the look Gideon was giving her. He was looking at her mouth with the lids half down over his eyes and his face was intent, as though it gave him deep pleasure to look at her like that.

It began softly, his lips coaxing hers, brushing them lightly. Then his hands went to her waist and drew her closer, enclosing her hands against his chest. His mouth moved delicately and she found her own parting. Gideon breathed faster. One hand moved up and down her back, fingering the fine bones, shaping her body against him. He was kissing her in a new way now. His other hand gripped the back of her head, tilting it backward, and he began to kiss her hungrily, the hard mouth demanding response.

She gasped at the change, a restless fluttering deep inside her, as though her nerves were going wild with pleasure. Her hands wriggled to free themselves and then slid round his neck, her finger-tips touching the smooth skin, feeling his neck muscles tautening under her touch.

Gideon lifted his mouth to look at her. She leaned against him, flushed and trembling, her blue eyes shyly meeting his gaze. There was something of a question in his look, as though he were waiting for an answer to an unspoken question. Marina did not know what the question was and could not answer, but it seemed that her submissive look was the answer Gideon wanted, because after a moment he brought his mouth down again with a hunger which tore through her body with the shock of a blow.

He sat down in Grandie's armchair with her on his lap and kissed her deeply, one hand running over her relaxed body. It never even entered her head to be horrified or alarmed by the fondling movement of that hand. Gideon was caressing her shoulders, her breasts, her waist, and she was not protesting or finding anything novel or terrifying in what he was doing. She clasped her arms behind his dark head and sighed with pleasure.

The door opened suddenly. Gideon's hand lay on her breast, his fingers splayed sensually, the tips stroking her. He lifted his black head and slowly took his hand away. Marina felt hot colour rushing into her face. She tried to sit up on Gideon's lap, throwing a horrified look at the door, but Gideon restrained her firmly.

'Goodnight,' Grandie said brusquely. The door shut.

Marina stared at it and turned her incredulous eyes on Gideon. He lay back in the chair, watching her.

She was sensitive to every tiny mood of her grandfather. She had lived alone with him for too long not to catch each flicker of feeling or thought in him. She had felt just now that Grandie was angry, that he was shocked. He had not said a word, yet she had heard his unspoken protest at what he had seen. Yet he had gone without saying anything. She probed Gideon's glittering black eyes for a clue. Why had Grandie said nothing? Why had he merely gone out silently?

Gideon revealed nothing to her questioning eyes. He gave her a strange little smile. 'Bedtime, I think,' he said, and she could not fail to hear the reluctance in his voice, the deep tone which held an aroused passion.

In her own room she undressed and got into her bed, listening to the movements from Gideon's room, the creak of the ancient floorboards, the tiny sound of him winding his watch. She had her curtains drawn back. Moonlight streamed into the room like silent dust settling on all the furniture and silvering it. The sea was running softly tonight, a slow sad whisper far away as it began to withdraw once more.

Emma and Meg sat upright at the end of the bed. In the moonlight their faces had a listening awareness. 'Is he blackmailing Grandie?' Marina asked them. Her toes made little bumps under the bedclothes and she wiggled them thoughtfully. 'If he was, wouldn't Grandie hate him? And he doesn't. Tonight he smiled at Gideon several times as though he liked him. But although he likes him he seems bothered by him. It isn't as if Grandie is afraid of him, more as if he's worried by something about him.'

Her cheeks went pink as she remembered the way Gideon had kissed and caressed her. It had seemed so natural and right, as though it had happened many times before. Those long fingers had known their way around her body and her body had known their touch.

'It's creepy,' she said with a shiver. 'It must be reincarnation.' She felt the silent laughter of the dolls and made a face at them. 'Well, there has to be some explanation.'

Closing her eyes, she listened to the sea and gradually fell asleep, but it was a restless sleep. The moonlight lay upon her lids and filled her inner eye with dreams. She dreamt she was flying, floating, oddly weightless and free, the wind in her long hair.

Then she stood in a room and stared through the moonlight at a bed. Gideon sat up from a sleep-tossed sheet. It slid off him and she saw his shoulders bare, gleaming smoothly in the pale light. She floated over a floor she never touched and knelt on the bed, her eyes on his body. He wasn't speaking or moving. The heavy lids were way back from his eyes and they were gleaming like dark wells, watching her. She sank back on her heels, putting out a hand. It gently touched his shoulder, felt the roundness of the shoulderbone, fingered along the collarbone as though she were playing the piano.

Gideon's hand moved then, reaching up to play with the loose silvery hair which blew in a cool wind.

They touched each other in a silence which was free of emotion. Gideon drew her down on the bed and she sighed. All their movements had a sensual delicacy which in the dream was like a slow-motion film, each caress precise and studied, with the consciousness of an action often repeated.

His mouth moved on hers and she began to tremble, her hands holding the black head. Gideon suddenly rolled on top of her, pressing her down into the bed.

There was an ache inside her body, a burning dissolving sweetness which was also pain. Gideon lay on her, breathing hoarsely now, so that the roughly drawn sound of his intake of air filled her ears. His mouth touched her throat. He kissed her shoulders quickly, hurriedly, each touch of his mouth moving onward, downward until his face was buried between her breasts, then he was moving against her restlessly, his hands sliding down her body.

She opened her eyes as though her lids were heavy. Gideon's head lifted and his eyes were blind in the moonlight although his eyes were open. The pressure of desire seemed to be forcing itself against the inside of her skull, fountaining into her head from deep within her body.

They were neither of them saying a word. Their limbs moved in naked smoothness, clinging. Marina ran her hands down his long, smooth back and felt the tension of his muscles tighten, then Gideon gave a wild, harsh moan and they were melting, their arms around each other, their faces cheek to cheek, their breathing sharp and agonised with pleasure.

She revolved in waves of passion, hearing his cries like echoes of her own, questioning nothing, unafraid and unsurprised. The release came like drowning. She sank, slackening, a long sigh on her lips, and Gideon lay on her, shaking. It seemed a long time before either of them moved again.

Then she was floating again, her arms around his neck. He kissed her gently and laid her down. The dream folded like a flower at nightfall.

When she woke up the dream came back into her mind at once, sharp as a thorn, and her face flowered in hot colour. She put her hands over her eyes, shamed and horrified. She had never had such a dream in her life. Through her fingers she saw the dolls staring bolt-eyed at her. Disapproving, prim, they sat with turned-up toes in the morning sunlight.

'It didn't happen,' she said to them crossly. 'Can I help my dreams?'

What were dreams? The adventures of the subconscious when it was freed by sleep? During the day the conscious mind kept tight hold of the body, reining it like a troublesome horse, but in sleep it lost its dominance and the subconscious poured from its hiding place like smoke, like a genie from a bottle.

'Stop staring at me!' Marina said to the dolls, and

jumped out of bed. Her skin this morning felt cool and alive. She was aware of a relaxation of some tension. Dressed, she went downstairs and Gideon was reading over a cup of coffee, his black head bent. He looked round, smiling casually, and she felt her face colour at the sight of him, but there was no answering consciousness in his features.

If he knew! she thought, trying to make herself as calm as he was, somehow smiling back at him.

'I heard Mr Grandison moving half an hour ago,' he said. 'I took him some coffee, but he isn't coming down. He feels tired.'

She looked worried. 'He isn't ill?'

Gideon glanced at her. 'He's in his seventies. It can't be expected he'll leap around like a spring lamb.'

She gave a little sigh. 'Don't!' Grandie was her whole life. She could not bear to think of him as being old.

Gideon looked at her carefully. 'I don't think you need to fret. He's still very healthy. Apart from his rheumatism he's sound for years. But pain is tiring, Marina, and he's in constant pain.'

'I know.' She sat down and looked at him unhappily. 'It's so awful not being able to do anything about it.'

'You are doing something about it,' Gideon said gently. 'Just by being yourself. Grandie is living through you. When he listens to you playing he's living again.'

She knew that and was worried by it. Grandie hoped for too much from her. He burdened her with the pressure of his hope. He set her an impossible standard. Nothing short of perfection, and Marina was afraid of failing him.

Gideon was watching her. Their eyes met and she had a curious feeling that he could read her thoughts. It was not the first time she had felt that. He touched her hand briefly.

'He's very proud of you. You've given his life new meaning.'

His voice had a quiet authority. He sounded as if he knew exactly how Grandie felt, knew things she did not see how he could know. He was a stranger to them, yet he spoke as one vested in authority. Marina frowned.

'Tell me the truth, Gideon.'

Her voice pleaded and he stared at her without a flicker of expression.

'What do you mean?'

She gestured with her pale hands. 'What is the truth? Have you and Grandie met before? I'm not stupid—I know there's something strange going on since you came.'

He got up and looked at her searchingly. 'Marina, do you trust me?'

Eyes widening, she stared into the hard dark face. There was the slightest pause. Then she said with a sigh, 'Yes.'

She did trust him. How could she fail to do so when his eyes were so cool and steady, his mouth strong and firm? He was a man on whom one could trust, her instincts told her that.

He smiled and his face held a warmth and charm which reached inside her and touched her heart. 'Then trust me now,' he said. 'No harm will ever

come to you and Grandie from me, I promise you.'
Turning away, he said: 'I waited for you to come
down, but I'm starving. What shall we have for
breakfast?'

They had freshly squeezed orange juice and
scrambled eggs. Gideon did the scrambling while
Marina made the toast. They worked together com-
patibly, smiling at each other now and then, and she
felt his tall lithe figure had been a part of her life
for years.

After breakfast she tidied the house, a piece of
ribbon tying back her loose hair. She was wearing
jeans and a T-shirt and Ruffy kept catching the
turn-up of her jeans and worrying it between his
teeth.

'He wants a walk,' she said.

Gideon came over to her and untied the ribbon,
brushing out her hair over her shoulders. 'Then
let's take him for one,' he said.

Ruffy tore ahead over the cliff paths, barking, his
tail wagging furiously. The gulls wheeled over his
head and below him the sea lay in a milky calm,
sunlight dancing on the water.

When they had gone as far as Spanish Head they
walked down through a copse heady with wild
garlic, the thick strange scent of it unpleasant in
such quantity. Old hornbeams twisted in weird
shapes around them.

'Wheelwrights used to use them,' said Gideon,
tapping a bough with one long finger. 'They found
the shapes useful. That's probably why they're
dying out—nobody needs them any more.'

Marina shivered. 'What a sad thought. Poor trees!'

He gave her a wry little smile. 'We all have to be needed.'

She looked away, her skin heating, remembering her dream when Gideon had said thickly, 'I need you.' Glancing at him through her lashes she saw a little gleam in the black eyes as he watched her. He could not imagine what she was thinking, but she coloured even more, looking away.

As she walked faster, as though to evade those memories, her hair caught on a gnarled finger of hornbeam, its contortions reminiscent of Grandie's twisted hands. She yelped, her hand going to her hair.

'Stand still,' Gideon ordered.

Marina stood docilely while he released her, then he turned her towards him. The shadows of the trees flickered over his face. He held her shoulders gently, smiling.

She was afraid to have him kiss her; she was terrified of what that kiss might reveal to him. Already her lips were burning in anticipation, the memory of those dream kisses swelling under her smooth skin.

She swung hurriedly to escape, and his hands tightened, turning her back to him.

She threw a look up at his face. His eyes were narrowed in a cool speculation, watching her intently. He bent his head and kissed her with demanding intensity, his hands holding her close.

Marina felt an answering hunger. She kissed him back with an eagerness she could not hide and as he lifted his head his face had a satisfaction which infuriated her.

'Don't fight me, Marina,' he whispered, a smile curving his mouth. 'Relax.'

'You mustn't,' she muttered, pulling away.

'Why mustn't I?'

She threw a bewildered look at him. 'I've only known you for two days.'

'Two days, two years … does it matter?'

'Of course it does!'

'Why?' he asked softly.

She sought for an answer and could not find one. Huskily, she said. 'I'm eighteen. How old are you?'

His face altered. 'Thirty-seven,' he said, and there was a hard ring to his voice. She saw she had touched on something to which he was sensitive. His eyes were restless now, a frown etched between them.

'Twice my age,' she said quietly.

He stared at her, and there was tautness in the set of his mouth. 'Does that bother you?'

'Doesn't it bother you?' She saw it did. He could not hide it. His eyes were very dark and angry.

'Are you married?' she asked huskily, because could a man as attractive as Gideon have reached his age without marrying?

There was a silence. Gideon looked at her with a spot of dark red burning on each cheek. After a moment, he said, 'No,' and she knew he had lied. It was in his eyes.

'No?' she asked very quietly, letting her scornful stare tell him she knew he was lying.

He moved, his face restless. Again he paused and

at last he lifted his shoulders in a half-angry shrug. 'Not now.'

'But you were?'

He nodded curtly, about to turn away, but she had to know the whole truth. It had only been a dream last light, but it had revealed to her how deeply he had penetrated her subconscious.

'Is she alive? I mean, are you divorced or ...'

'Separated,' he said harshly with a black frown, and Marina felt her spirits dive into a depression. That woman, she thought. Was that her? It would explain everything. His anger, his coldness, the woman's distress and passion. Did he still love her beneath that frown of his?

Gideon was staring at her and she could see the disturbed emotion in the glittering black eyes. He put out his hand to touch her cheek, stroking down the smooth flushed curve of it tenderly. 'Forget it,' he said huskily. 'It doesn't affect you and me. Believe me, Marina, I would die rather than hurt you.'

He moved closer and his eyes moved down to her mouth with that look in his face, a look which deepened to a burning intensity as he came closer.

'No,' she said, moving back hastily. 'Don't!'

'I must,' he said thickly. 'You know I must.' His arms came round her and wouldn't let her go. She heard him breathing in her hair, his chest wrenched by emotion, his lungs hoarsely drawing air and expelling it at a pace which sounded frantic.

'Marina,' he murmured with his lips against her ear. 'Oh, Marina!' His mouth pushed down her cheek and found her mouth. After a short struggle she surrendered to his possession of it with a little groan.

They stood in the shadows embracing closely, kissing each other so deeply that she felt she was being absorbed into his bloodstream and he into hers.

He let her go reluctantly, his eyes passionate. Ruffy was barking somewhere and Gideon grimaced. 'We'd better see what he's up to,' he said. There was a smile on his face as they walked out of the copse. He was holding her hand, swinging it.

Ruffy was leaping around the vicar like a dervish, his short white legs agile. For some reason he found the vicar's collar offensive. Grandie said it was because dogs are conservative by nature and do not like any departure from what they consider to be the norm. Whenever Ruffy saw the vicar he barked at him angrily, although the unfortunate man was both kind and friendly.

'Oh dear,' he said now, smiling at them. 'Ruffy will get me one day, I'm afraid.'

'Try putting your hand over your collar,' Gideon advised.

The vicar looked puzzled but obeyed and Ruffy sank back in satisfaction on his haunches, his pink tongue lolling in a pant of cheerful relaxation.

'Good heavens,' said the vicar, smiling. 'That was clever of you, Gideon.' His eyes touched on their linked hands and he looked at Marina with a smile. 'You're looking well, Marina. I'm very glad, very glad indeed.'

With a friendly nod he walked on and she looked at Gideon with a troubled frown. 'How did he know your name?'

Gideon looked coolly at her. 'Mrs Robinson?' he suggested.

Her brow cleared. 'Who else?'

They both laughed. On their way through the village, Mrs Dudeck put her head out of her door and said: 'I've got that dress ready to be fitted, Marina. Have you got time now? I could get on with it tonight then.'

Gideon smiled at them both. 'I'll take Ruffy back to the cottage. You have your fitting, Marina.'

'If you're sure,' she said doubtfully.

'I won't lose my way,' he said.

Mrs Dudeck laughed. 'Of course he won't.'

Her eye met Gideon's black glance and she stopped laughing and grew sober. Gideon walked away and Ruffy looked after him, ears pricked. Gideon gave a little whistle. Ruffy moved, paused and looked at Marina. 'Off you go,' she nodded. Ruffy grinned and tore after Gideon.

The fitting did not take long. Mrs Dudeck moved around with a mouth full of pins and talked through them without swallowing one. Her small sitting-room was crowded with ornaments including a garden gnome who sat on the top of the television with a cross, bored face.

She had no garden, only a short expanse of yard which she had had paved in multi-coloured stone tiles. 'My patio,' she called it, and liked to eat out there in the summer. It gave her the excuse for a long-running war with the neighbourhood cats. Each time she saw one crossing her precious patio she ran out screeching with flapping arms.

Her husband, Mr Dudeck, was an enormous man twice her size and was petrified of her. He had a deep rumbling voice and was as gentle as a lamb.

Mrs Dudeck bullied him in a high thin voice. They had no children, which was just as well since controlling Mr Dudeck took all his wife's energies.

'Dudeck will bring it up tomorrow,' she promised as Marina left. Mr Dudeck drove the baker's van which toured all the local villages. Slow-moving, slow-thinking, he enjoyed his job which kept him out in the open air and out from under Mrs Dudeck's feet. Marina always found it comical to see the great broad-shouldered man in the crowded little sitting-room, like an elephant in a china shop. He looked so uneasy, afraid that his elbow would dislodge one of his wife's beloved figures or his feet make one of the small mats crumple underfoot, but his face would shine with pride as his wife showed Marina her latest purchase. He eyed the brightly glazed little figures with delight. On the beauty of the ornaments he and his wife were at one, although Mr Dudeck was never allowed to touch one.

Marina walked quickly back to the cottage by a short cut and came in through the kitchen door. As she opened it she heard the piano. She knew it was not a recording; Marina was too familiar with the individual sound of her own piano to believe that. Her ears were very keen.

She stood outside the music room, frowning, incredulous. It couldn't be Grandie—that was impossible. Once he might have coaxed the keys to give forth this miraculous delicate sound, but that was long past, sunk in the depth of memory.

She had not come through the front door so she had not seen if there was a strange car parked outside.

They must have a visitor, she thought, racking her brains to recall a name to match this wonderful musical achievement. Someone from London, an old pupil of Grandie's—before his hands became quite useless he had had some pupils for a few years and all of them had gone on to become famous. Grandie only took the really promising ones.

She pushed open the music room door and froze on the threshold. Everything tore and rent inside her head. The room went dark and she saw figures moving through the darkness, but she was lost in it herself, soundlessly screaming, with parted lips which were bloodless and a face which was taut and stiff with pain.

CHAPTER FIVE

In the moments when she stood there Marina felt the merciful curtain come dragging down and she winced in the bitter light of what she now remembered.

The girl of eighteen she had imagined herself to be was dissolving like a fading dream. It was a woman who stared at Gideon as he tried to take her into his arms.

She fought away from him, giving deep little groans, as though she were someone drowning who refused to be saved, and fought off rescue in a panic and terror which no calming words could touch.

The piano still gave off that faint vibrating hum which came when music ended. No wonder he had refused to play for her, lying when he said he was not in her class!

Grandie thrust him aside and tried to put an arm round her, but she could not bear that, either. She felt as though she were shaking into pieces, her whole body shuddering. She wanted to be alone—not to be touched, to be free.

'Don't touch me!' she said hoarsely, and turned to run up the stairs into her own room, bolting the door and hearing their footsteps coming after her.

'My God, I warned you,' Grandie said thickly. 'Gideon, I warned you. I'll never forgive you.'

Gideon spoke close to the door, his voice pleading. 'Marina, let me in, darling. Let me in to talk to you. I've got to talk to you!'

'Go away,' she said in a voice which was not her own, a high still little voice, a child's, remote and cold.

It had been so easy in this quiet little backwater to slide back into the safe past, a past still untroubled by dreams. Now the dreams would come and she would have pain.

She sat down on the bed and wondered how she was going to bear it. Grandie and Gideon were talking outside. Gideon said suddenly, very loudly, 'I'll break the bloody door down!'

Grandie was angry, too, but his anger was with Gideon. 'This is still my house. Leave her alone!' He sounded like a man on the verge of doing something violent. 'If you'd left her alone in the first place this wouldn't be happening. You're as selfish as ever, Gideon.'

Marina stopped listening to them. Her mind was occupied with the bitter memories she had been trying to lock away for months. They poured into her like acid and she crouched on the bed, her hands over her eyes.

When she was eighteen, Grandie had taken her to London to take up a place at the Royal College of Music. Marina had not wasted her long years under Grandie's personal, unstinting tuition. In some ways she was more advanced than most of the other students and in others she had been a very shy, withdrawn girl who was almost entirely ignorant of the world in which she found herself. Her first months at the college had been a wild, dizzying whirl of new experiences. She kept Grandie in touch by letter and she made new friends, but it was still Grandie who was her only close friend, her mentor and her ally.

Just before the end of that first term, Grandie had come to London to hear a concert given by one of his pupils; one of the most brilliant pianists of the day. Afterwards he and Marina were going back to the cottage together. That evening she had sat in rapt intensity listening to music so perfectly executed and interpreted that she was deeply impressed. Grandie and several other friends whom they had met that evening took her on to a party afterwards. It was being given in honour of the pianist. He was knee-deep in excited women in the long cream and gold room. Marina shrank into a chair, terrified by all the people. Her upbringing had made London an ordeal for her. She detested noise, she feared crowds.

Now she sat on a chair and stared at the black head, watching the movements of the tall lean body, listened to the occasional note she caught of his deep voice.

Once as he moved he caught sight of her and looked at her. Marina was so nervous that she looked away, clasping her hands in her lap.

He was talking when she looked again. A woman with wreathed silky black hair hung on his arm, smiling at him, the languid sensuous lines of her body betraying to Marina's stare that she was in love with him. As she watched she saw his sinewy hand slide down the woman's shoulder and arm, saw him smile into her eyes, and she knew then that Gideon Firth was the woman's lover. Her innocence of passion had been somewhat rudely shattered when she arrived at the college. All her fellow students seemed to lead exciting lives. Marina had no time for love, but she learnt to recognise the look of it, to comprehend the emotions behind the way someone touched the person next to them.

Grandie had come over to collect her, smiling. 'Now why did you hide away like that?'

He knew her shyness and was indulgent with it. His arm around her he led her towards the door. Gideon Firth stopped them before they reached it. He turned his glittering eyes on Marina and she looked into his hard, sensual face and saw the uplifted excitement of the performance still on him. He was reckless with it, his mouth smiling widely.

'You haven't introduced me, Grandie,' he said.

Grandie smiled, pleased. 'Gideon, this is my granddaughter. Marina, Gideon Firth.'

Gideon held out his hand and she shakily put her own into the strong fingers. Holding her hand, he had bent that dark face on her with a confident, piercing smile.

'Marina,' he repeated. 'Incredible!' He spread her fingers out over his palm. 'You play, of course.'

Grandie laughed and began to tell him about her while she stood with a flushed face and downcast eyes, so conscious of Gideon that she could not look at him.

They were interrupted a moment later by the dark woman who twined herself against Gideon with the assurance of one who has a claim to such familiarity. Once Marina looked up and the woman's cold eyes assessed and dismissed her with a flick from head to foot. Hot-cheeked, Marina did not look up again.

They left, and Marina was silent all the way back to the hotel at which Grandie was staying. She had a room there too for the night.

'He could be a great pianist,' said Grandie, nodding, as they were on their way home next day.

'Could be?' she repeated in disbelief. 'He is!'

Grandie's mouth went straight, wryness in the shape of it. 'He's technically amazing and very clever, but the feeling ... it's too much on the surface, a mimicry of the thing, not the thing itself.'

Marina stared at him, remembering the fluent ease and delicacy of the playing. Was he right?

'He's too hard,' Grandie added. 'Too certain.'

She remembered Gideon's elevation after the concert, his triumph and glitter, and sensed that Grandie might be right.

Christmas came with a bitterly cold spell of weather. Marina wore a little circle in the frost on the window pane by leaning against it, her nose pressed to the cold glass, her breath slowly thawing the brittle crystals. The grass was stiff and silvered, the roofs glistening, the cats walking over icy ground with a pained expression.

Grandie gave her a white fur muff and hood for Christmas. She put them on for the first time to walk along the cliff paths and watch the sea coldly breaking on the stones.

Two days after Christmas she was playing absorbedly when she felt someone in the room behind her. Glancing over her shoulder, expecting Grandie, she met Gideon Firth's black eyes.

Her hands stiffened and fell still.

'Go on,' he said, sinking into a chair.

She shook her head, hurriedly getting up from the stool. 'Does Grandie know you're here?' Her voice sounded unlike itself, thin and high.

'He told me to come in and listen,' Gideon said softly, staring at her. 'I'm here. So sit down and play to me.'

She gave him a half-frightened look. 'I couldn't!'

His brows rose. 'You play at the college. Why not to me?'

She didn't know why, only that she did not want to have him sit there and listen to her. Hurriedly escaping into the kitchen, she put on her red cloak, muff and hood and went out into the frosty air.

Grandie did not say anything, just looked at her with affectionate amusement.

Walking along the cliff path, she heard twigs breaking behind her and looked round to find Gideon at her heels. Her face coloured.

'Hallo, Red Riding Hood,' he said mockingly. 'I'm the wolf.'

She had a self-protective flare of annoyance. 'My hood's white,' she pointed out.

He joined her and looked down into her face. 'So it is,' he said softly, his hard mouth curling. 'And very charming, too.'

The kiss was light and teasing, a kiss for a child, and she pulled away with a racing heart and a sense of danger.

Gideon took her arm, his hand curling round it possessively. 'Where shall we walk? There ought to be a wood,' he said, still teasing.

They walked along the cliff paths to Spanish Headland and stood in silence staring out into the tumultuous seas, hearing the wind whip flailingly across the tops of the waves and churn them into white foam.

'Real Wagner weather,' Gideon commented.

On the way back to the cottage he complained of the cold and slid one of his hands inside her muff. 'What warm little fingers,' he said as he found them. Marina felt his index finger stroking her palm and a shiver ran down her back.

Grandie had made coffee, and Gideon drank it gratefully, shivering. When his hands had warmed up he played to them, and now Marina could hear what Grandie had meant. In the concert hall the brilliance of the finish had obscured it for her, but now she heard the polished hardness overlaying the music and she was disturbed. It revealed the man, she thought, watching him.

Gideon swung to look at her in the little silence that followed. She looked at him with wide, distressed eyes and saw a frown pull his black brows together.

He searched her face and the frown deepened. Rising, he gestured. 'Now you,' he said with a terse parting of his mouth.

Marina sat down and stared at the trees beyond the window. For a few moments she did not touch the keys. She breathed quietly, thinking. Gideon made an abrupt movement and Grandie put a hand on his arm. The black head swung and Gideon looked at him. Grandie shook his head.

Marina played, aware at one level of her mind of the many threads of technique which she was holding at the back of her head, and at another level aware of what the music needed, allowing herself to become the reed through which the wind blew, her body flowing into the piano as though it were part of it, an extension of it. Submerged in the music, she had no personality, no claims to identity. All her technique was used merely to free the music and let it exist. Marina did not exist.

When the notes fell into silence she sat with her hands in her lap, drained, still empty of thought, a discarded vessel.

Grandie got up and kissed her cheek, then went out. Marina did not turn to look at Gideon. She could hear him breathing behind her, but he was not moving. After a long time he got up and went out too without saying a word.

When she went into the kitchen later he had gone. Grandie never mentioned to her anything Gideon had said, so she did not know whether he had been pleased or indifferent.

He did not come again that holiday. She returned to college and a few months later Gideon came to give the prizes away at their speech day. Marina was trembling as she went up to receive hers. Gideon handed it to her, his eye skating over her. He gave her a little nod of recognition but made no personal comment. She was surprised afterwards at the sherry party which followed that he came up to her.

'How's Grandie?' he asked.

'Very well,' she said politely.

Gideon looked at her with restless eyes, their movement over her flickering lightly. 'Will you have dinner with me tomorrow?'

The question sounded almost nervous, which was ridiculous because he was a world-famous artist and she was a shy nineteen-year-old.

She looked away, flushing. For a few seconds she hesitated, knowing instinctively the dangers of saying yes. Her eyes came up to his face.

Gideon was watching her. Their eyes held. 'Thank you,' she said slowly.

That first evening he had talked of Grandie and then of music, his taste in it inclining to the music he played best himself, music which gave scope to his power and verve. Marina said very little. She listened with her eyes on his hard face and her features betrayed her inner hesitance about him.

He did not make any attempt to touch her. He drove her back to the hostel in which she was living and said goodnight, then Marina went in and felt the weariness of someone who has been under strain for a long time. Gideon tired her. When she was with him she felt as though he were an electric light shone directly into her eyes. She was guarding herself against it, but the tension of keeping up her shield was exhausting.

Like any international musician he spent a good deal of time out of the country. When he was in England and had some free time, he began to see Marina regularly, but those evenings came so infrequently that she forgot between each occasion just how much of a strain it was to be with him, and when he came back like a homing pigeon she accepted invitations recklessly.

She was torn now between a deep attraction and an equally deep fear of him. Marina was ultra-sensitive, yielding by nature, someone who gave of herself, to music or to the people she cared for, but because she was so fragile in identity she had to protect herself. She was learning how easily Gideon could hurt her and how deep that hurt could go.

They never spoke of his private life, but in musical circles it was open knowledge that he had a long-standing affair with Diana Grenoby.

It had given Marina a shock to find the woman's face staring at her from an opera programme one evening. She had read the biography under that beautiful, sophisticated face with intent absorption. It had not mentioned Gideon, of course, but it had given Marina an insight into the older woman's life-style.

Diana Grenoby was a soprano with a lovely voice, and when Marina heard her sing she was inevitably impressed but could sense that Diana had the same polished gloss which made Gideon so impressive and yet so lacking in final satisfaction. There was no music in either of them, she told herself. Music was feeling. The technique had to be there, of course; it was the foundation of the house. But the technique could not make up for a lack of sensitivity, humanity, and that was what both Gideon and Diana Grenoby revealed in their performances. It was why Diana, although the owner of a beautiful voice and a dazzling beauty, had never become a really great singer.

Gossip columns occasionally gave Marina a glimpse of Gideon's relations with Diana. He was seen with her from time to time and although the newspapers were discreetly veiled about their relationship, Marina's friends at the college filled in the bare details for her without ever realising that she was personally involved.

'There've been other women,' one girl said, yawning. Marina had never hinted to them that she knew Gideon personally. To them it was all fascinating gossip about a star they admired. 'But she's lasted the longest. Not surprising—she's a very sexy lady, they say.'

Marina had said nothing, but winced.

Marina was working absorbedly at the college, most of her waking hours spent in learning, practising, untired of constant repetition and the need to be as close to perfection as one could. When she was not with Gideon she shut him out of her mind. He was an unresolved problem. She had not permitted herself to admit just how much of a problem he was, but as the months passed and she saw more and more of him, the problem grew.

She knew he was still seeing Diana Grenoby, but they had never mentioned that name. Gideon was keeping his evenings with Marina on a level which excluded any necessity to admit or deny commitment. He never kissed her. He never touched her. They talked and listened to music, they saw films or had dinner, they walked in the London parks and went to the theatre. It was a friendship, nothing more, and had Gideon been a boy of her own age Marina would have felt no qualms.

Gideon, though, was both much older and far more experienced. He never took her to his London flat. Their meetings always took place on public ground, a safe venue where they were never really alone.

One evening at the end of the following autumn she was at the opera when she saw Gideon in the stalls with Diana. The two of them were talking animatedly, laughing, and Marina saw the physical intimacy between them even more sharply than she had the first time she saw them together.

It drove a thorn into her. She sat with the music assaulting her ears and wanted to cry. I love him, she thought, watching that black head in the dark auditorium.

She did not sleep that night. She lay awake and faced the problem that had haunted her for months. Her relationship with Gideon was based on shifting sand. It could only hurt her. Whatever he wanted from her could never be enough. She had to end it before she got hurt even more.

He rang two days later, and she gently regretted that she couldn't see him during the week he was to be in London. 'I'm booked every day,' she told him.

Gideon sounded curt. 'I see. Well, next time I come back.'

'That would be nice,' she returned without over-enthusiasm.

He rang off and she cried, but her working life had taught her to protect herself against outside things that could destroy her concentration and she turned those lessons to good use. Gideon flew round the world playing in various capitals and while he was away Marina finally accepted her first date with someone of her own age.

He was a violinist at the college, a thin sensitive boy a year older than herself. They had known each other since her first day at the college and Paul had often invited her out, but she had politely made excuses. Now she agreed and began to date him once a week. They got free tickets to recitals and competitions, discussed music avidly, endlessly. Marina was often with him at the college since they worked in the same groups. She enjoyed his company. They were careful with each other, making progress slowly, neither wishing to hurry into a relationship from which they could not draw back.

When Gideon got back he rang her. They had not seen each other or spoken for three months. She spent some time congratulating him on the success of his tour. 'I read a lot of rave notices. You must be very pleased.'

'Will you have dinner with me tonight?' he asked when she had run out of things to say.

'Oh, dear, I would have loved to,' she said, her voice a little too careful. 'But I have a date, I'm afraid.'

Gideon was silent. 'Tomorrow?'

'I wish I could,' Marina said on a sigh. 'But I'm rehearsing—did I tell you I'm playing for a lieder performance? Accompanying a girl with the most fantastic voice. I'm sure she's going places. You like lieder, don't you?'

'What's wrong, Marina?' Gideon asked abruptly.

She bit her lip. 'What do you mean?' Her laughter was false and she knew he must hear that. 'Nothing. I really would have loved to see you. Oh, that's the bell—I must go, I'm afraid. Goodbye, Gideon.'

She put the phone down as though it had burnt her and leaned her face on the glass of the booth in the students' hall. After a moment she pulled herself together and managed to make light conversation with the group who were talking nearby, marvelling that the anguish she felt did not show on her face.

Two days later she and Paul were queueing for gallery tickets to see a West End play when Gideon walked past with Diana Grenoby. Marina did not look round at him, but she heard the deep dark tone of his voice just behind her and Diana Grenoby's answering laughter.

It was ironic, she thought, seated in the front row of the gallery beside Paul and aware that Gideon was in a box opposite with the dark sleek

head of Diana beside him. The situation was sym-
bolic of their positions in life and it escaped her
why Gideon had ever bothered to see her at all, even
on the casual, friendly level on which their relationship had existed.

After the play when the lights went up Paul
guided her up the steep stairs to the back of the
gallery, his arm lightly round her waist. She was
so weary of pain that she leant her head on his
shoulder and felt his arm tighten.

'You look tired,' Paul said in concern. 'You work
too hard—you always have. Everyone says you
should relax more. There's no doubt in anyone's
mind where you're going, so why the need to strain
to get there?'

'Why, indeed?' she said wryly, without comment-
ing on the compliment. Her teachers had made it
plain that they, too, expected her to do well. She
was burdened with Grandie's reputation, with his
dreams for her, with the demands of other people's
high expectations. She had worked obsessively ever
since she got to college and the pain which Gideon
had caused her had nagged inside her all the time,
weakening her.

Paul was a very serious young man and he had
become fond of her. When the holidays began she
took him back to stay with Grandie. They had a
lot of fun that spring, walking along the beach,
paddling in the chill water, throwing stones across
the waves so that they skipped and bounced with
little splashes, giving mock concerts to Grandie,
playing like music hall artists to him, so that he
laughed and rocked in his chair.

Gideon did not get in touch with her again, but later in the summer he sent her two tickets for one of his London concerts with a brief and distant little note.

She took Paul. They had excellent seats with a clear view of Gideon. Marina stared at him as he played, seeing a new fine tension to his hard face, hearing a change in his music. Gideon was digging below the surface now. Grandie should have heard it, she thought. The polish and brilliant technique were still there, but there was a new feeling in the playing. It was a change reflected in his body. When he took his applause he was obviously thinner. He had never been less than fit, but now his bones showed through the brown skin, the harshness of them taut.

As he straightened from a deep bow with the enthusiasm roaring around him undiminished, his black eyes slid briefly to where Marina sat. She was sitting there with her eyes riveted on him and for a second their eyes met. Feeling flashed across the hall between them. She had never seen it in his eyes before, but now she saw it and her heart stopped.

Gideon had looked at her hungrily with the eyes of a frustrated lover, and she was trembling as he walked from the platform.

She had to leave with Paul, trying to control herself, trying to appear normal while every particle of her mind and body was overthrown with the realisation of what she had glimpsed so briefly in Gideon's eyes.

She did not know what to do. She couldn't sleep,

couldn't work. Had she imagined it? Was it all in her own mind?

She came down the steps of the college at five o'clock next day and Gideon straightened from the wall and looked at her. He didn't say a word, but her heart began to beat fiercely and she was totally unaware of the people behind her streaming out of the door; staring as they recognised Gideon and then Marina and buzzing with curiosity.

There seemed to be nothing they could either of them find to say; there was too much to be said in words. Gideon took her to his flat for the first time and when they were alone he looked at her with that strange, fixed intensity and broke out: 'Why have you kept me away all these months? What's wrong? Why wouldn't you see me?'

She stared at her feet, her neck bent in a wistful curve. 'Does it matter?'

'Matter?' He rasped the word hoarsely. 'Don't you know it does?' He took a step and caught her shoulders, staring at her with that heat burning deep inside the black eyes. 'Who was that boy you were with? Is it him? Is he why you've shut me out?'

She looked up in disbelief, her eyes wide in amazement, and saw his dark face flush slowly under her stare. He pivoted, shuddering, as though wrenched by feelings he could not control, and Marina watched the broad shoulders and couldn't believe what she knew she was seeing.

'Are you in love with him?'

He asked the question in a low, controlled voice, but every muscle in his body was tense. She could see a nerve leaping in his cheek as he stood with his back to her but his face in profile.

She was torn by contradictory instincts. She could lie and let him believe she did not love him or she could tell him the truth and leave herself wide open to him.

When she didn't answer, Gideon swerved to look at her in harsh probing and as their eyes met, Marina trembled. She didn't say a word, but Gideon drew a deep breath and his hands reached out for her. That first kiss told him all the things she had tried to hide from him. Even now, with her body shaking in his arms and her soft mouth totally responsive to the fierce hot possession of his, she was trying to fight down her love for him. Young as she was, she knew the danger of letting him see how vulnerable she was to him. Gideon wanted her— she knew that now. He was jealous of Paul and he hadn't hidden it from her. But Marina had spent too many hours watching him, thinking about him, not to know that Gideon was not yet capable of love as she knew it.

That night it didn't matter, though. Gideon was on fire, and the flames licked into her blood and consumed her. She had no thought of denying him anything. He was gentle and tender, touching her with shaking hands, and moaning huskily as their bodies merged with a slow insistence which had been inevitable from the moment he touched her.

The strained tautness had left his face as she lay dazedly in his arms later. He stroked her face and kissed her. Marina was not yet capable of thinking. She had abandoned herself to him knowing what she was doing and no longer caring that he might destroy her. She had fought her love for him, but she could not fight Gideon's desire for her.

'Does this Paul mean anything?' he asked her abruptly, and she felt a weakness inside her at the unhidden jealousy. She shook her head.

'Don't see him again.' He held her face between his hands and stared at her as if each time he saw her he could not quite believe she was real. 'I can't bear to see you with him.'

She did not point out that she could not bear to see him with Diana Grenoby. She did not say anything. Gideon had not said a word which might indicate that he loved her, even during the moments of their fierce lovemaking. She had learnt how to hide her feelings. Although she was aching with the pain she had suspected for so long that he would give her, she hid it now.

Over the next few weeks they saw each other whenever they were both free. It was not often enough for Marina and although he did not say so she guessed it was not often enough for Gideon, either. When she was in his arms he was hotly demanding. However intense their passion grew, though, he never gave her any reason to hope that she meant more to him than any other woman who had lain in his bed. They made love in a heated silence which left her starving for a word, an admission of love.

He flew away to perform from time to time and often tried to persuade her to go with him, but she always refused. She would not let him treat her as his mistress in front of strangers or friends—their relationship was as yet a total secret and Marina felt sick at the idea of anyone else knowing.

She did not know if he was still seeing Diana. He never mentioned her. Marina spent bitter moments wondering about that. When he was not in her bed, where was he?

She went home to Basslea when the holidays next began. Grandie stared at her, his rough brows meeting, and she knew he could read the changes in her face which her relationship with Gideon had begun. All of the child left in her had gone. It was a woman who looked back at Grandie now, a woman eaten with passion and sadness she could not hide.

When Gideon walked in, Grandie knew at a glance. Alone with her, he asked her bitterly, 'Are you out of your mind? You know what he's like. Gideon's hard, as hard as nails. He'll get tired of you and leave you flat.'

'I know,' she said with bitter irony.

'Then why?' Grandie was incredulous at her resignation.

'I love him,' Marina told him, and that silenced him.

He said nothing to him, but he treated Gideon with icy hostility from that brief conversation. Marina was sorry that Grandie should be so hurt and angry, but she was aware that part of Grandie's anger was because Gideon was absorbing her energy, her spirit, and Grandie wanted all that to go into her music. Gideon was a threat to Grandie's dream for her.

Walking along the cliffs with him, listening to him play in the evenings, she had time to think deeply about Gideon and to recognise his self-preservation in all his relationships. He surrounded himself with a wall of silence because he refused to risk all that love could mean.

Had he ever loved Diana? Or anyone?

Teasing her about the dolls he came close to the verge of real anger, telling her sharply that she was too old for such childish games, looking at them with hostile dark eyes, and she wondered if Gideon had ever been a child. He had been a prodigy at the age of seven: she knew that.

Grandie had told her about his mother's pride and smothering adoration of him, painting a picture of a small boy treated as a god and yet a plaything, a status symbol for a ruthless woman.

Gideon had to go to America soon after term began. That time he almost begged her to go with him, using coaxing, threats, argument. Marina fought his need to have her with him because she felt, instinctively, that she could not allow him to treat her as a possession. Gideon had to come to recognise her as a human being with dignity of her own.

While he was away she realised she was pregnant. The shock sent her running back to Basslea and there Grandie looked at her with hatred, because she had destroyed his dreams for her. White-faced, she faced the ruin of all that they had both worked for and could find nothing to say to him.

'He won't marry you!' Grandie had shouted.

Marina did not need to be told that. Gideon had never breathed a word of marriage. He didn't love her; why should he marry her? She had walked into this with her eyes open. She would have to deal with it.

Grandie suggested an abortion and she shrank. She could not destroy Gideon's child. Her misery touched Grandie at last and he softened. 'We'll manage, darling,' he said, patting her as if she were still a child. 'We'll manage.'

She went to stay with friends of his who ran a home for handicapped children. Marina helped them and found some sort of solace in doing things for other people. It took her mind off her own misery—her problems seemed less heavy compared to those she saw around her at the home.

While she was there, Grandie wrote to tell her Gideon was looking for her. He had been to Basslea and Grandie had refused to tell him where she was or what she was doing. 'He'll have to be told,' Grandie said in the letter. 'He won't take no for an answer.'

She wrote back, telling Grandie to let Gideon know the truth. 'But tell him I don't want to see him. I don't want anything from him. This is my problem, not his.'

Gideon arrived two days later. Marina was in the garden with a little boy when he walked out towards her. The air was filled with the scent of newmown grass and Marina stood there, feeling sick. She had not wanted to face him, but now she could not avoid it.

He looked down at her with those unreadable black eyes, his face harsh. 'Why did you try to keep it from me? How could you hide such a thing? I had the right to know.'

'It's my problem,' she said quietly. The little boy stared at them and she looked at him, forcing a smile. 'Go in and find the others, Colin. I'll be in later.'

He ran away in his ungainly stumble and Gideon said in a low, fierce voice, 'Your problem? It's my baby!'

'You don't want to get married or have responsibilities, do you, Gideon?' she asked with a pale smile. 'I knew that.'

His hands hurt as they clamped down on her shoulders. He pulled her against his body and his cheek brushed her hair. 'That's beside the point. It's my baby.' His lips touched her cheek. 'Marry me, Marina. I want to marry you. I didn't—I admit that. But I don't want to lose you. I want you—and the baby. I want you as my wife.'

She slackened in his arms, her body a weary cipher, and felt the burden of the lonely weeks without him slipping away. She had forced herself to face life without him and now she wasn't going to have to, and relief and happiness made her faint.

They were married at once and she moved into the London flat with him. Gideon seemed content with her permanent presence. When he had to go on tour again he took her with him. Their marriage seemed to be working. He looked for her as he began to play each night and when he came off, drenched and exhausted but still wound up to the point of nervous tension, her calming hand and smile seemed to soothe him and help him to climb down from the peak which he had climbed during the performance.

Once he apologised to her for having ruined her career. 'I could kick myself for my selfish stupidity! It should have occurred to me that you wouldn't have taken any precautions. I was just caught up in my own needs and I forgot yours. Darling, do you forgive me?'

She would have forgiven him anything. His playing had improved enormously, all the critics agreed. He was playing with depth and feeling now and the beautiful professional gloss did not need to cover any lack of sensitivity.

As her pregnancy advanced Marina looked a little tired and Gideon frowned over her pallor. 'This tour is too much for you. I think you should have a few weeks with Grandie to relax.'

'What about you?' She knew now that Gideon needed her there after a performance. He looked for her with an eager glance as he came off and the dark eyes gleamed with pleasure when he saw her.

'Never mind me,' he soothed, touching her cheek. 'You're such a tiny thing. I hate to see you look so tired. I'll hate being without you, but I'll bear it.'

The tenderness and caring were in his smile, deep in his dark eyes. She saw them and was satisfied, leaning her head on his strong body and knowing he cared for her. He had not yet said 'I love you', but she thought: one day he will. Perhaps he doesn't even know yet. Marina was beginning to believe he did love her and it was worth all the pain he had made her suffer in the past.

Gideon was oddly unaware, despite his sophistication. He was a man who had learnt to be arrogant, certain of himself, his great gifts making him indifferent to the feelings of others because as a young boy his mother had drummed it into him that he was 'different'. Marina had met her now and knew just what sort of woman she was—she had been met with cold, chilling dislike, the icy jealousy of one who resents someone else stepping into their place. It had not mattered because Gideon had long ago pushed his mother out of his life. Her possessive nature had made him defend himself by excluding her. But she had formed his character, all the same. Gideon had grown up worshipped and spoilt, given everything he wanted, taught to believe that he could do just as he chose without caring for the consequences.

The hard glossy shell around him had been there for years. Marina believed it was cracking. Gideon had learnt to love, but he did not know that himself even now.

While she stayed with Grandie she had plenty of time to think about Gideon and to see that her advent in his life had begun a change in him. Feeling had begun to surge in him and it was coming out in his music. How deep that feeling went, Marina could not guess. Her own love for him made it possible for her to understand him without hating him for the selfish arrogance which had taken her without ever meaning to love her.

Gideon came home from his tour and rang at once to say he would be coming to see her, but first he had a series of business matters to settle. He would come as soon as he could get away.

Marina was disappointed that he wasn't coming

at once, and Grandie laughed at her long face. 'Why not go up to London to him?' he suggested, and her eyes lit up.

Gideon had not suggested that because he did not want her tired by the journey, she guessed. She kissed Grandie. Gideon would be as happy to see her as she was to see him, she thought.

But she was wrong. When she let herself into their London flat she heard voices and as she opened the sitting-room door she felt a quiver of cold premonition before she even saw them.

Gideon sat on the couch and Diana Grenoby was in his arms, her hands framing his face. They were kissing passionately.

As the door opened they sprang apart and stared, and for a long moment Marina stared and stared, going so white her face lost every shred of life and colour. She felt herself falling down a deep dark well into a world which would mean nothing but misery for her from now on.

She turned and ran out again and the lift was there with the door open. She saw Gideon running as the door closed. His voice came hoarsely to her, but she didn't look at him.

London was in the grip of late homegoing traffic and she walked out of the building in a trance like a sleepwalker. She never even saw or heard the car she walked under.

When she did open her eyes to admit the world with a tearing reluctance the first face she saw was Gideon's, and she screamed and screamed as though he were a murderer. The nurses ran and people exclaimed all round her, but she was cowering like a child with her hands over her eyes. 'Take him away, take him away!'

That was the last thing she remembered, the light through her fingers and her own voice screaming, 'Take him away!'

She sat on the bed and stared at nothing, shaking. She had no idea how long it was since that day or what had happened. Somehow she had shut Gideon and time out of her head, passed back into the comfortable safe world of her childhood where nothing could reach or hurt her again.

CHAPTER SIX

GRANDIE spoke at the door, quietly, persuasively. 'The doctor is here, darling. Please, see him.'

Marina slowly got off the bed and went to the door. Grandie looked at her with grey anxiety and she gave him a dry little smile. 'I'm all right now.'

The doctor stood behind him, watching her. She had known him all her life and he had never given her a clue over the last months that there was anything hidden in her life. Looking back, she recognised the conspiracy of silence which the whole village had entered into and was touched by the thought and affection behind it.

'Shall we have a look at you, Marina?' the doctor asked, coming forward and smiling at her.

'I'm fine.'

'We'll see, shall we?' He was being very careful not to distress her, but his voice was firm. He led her back into the bedroom and closed the door, excluding Grandie.

She sat down on the bed, glad to sit down because her legs were trembling. Her head felt heavy as though it did not belong to her and was not too well balanced on her neck.

The doctor took her pulse, his eyes on her face, careful searching eyes that probed her pale features.

'How do you feel?' he asked.

'I told you—fine.' She gave him a hard little smile. 'How do you expect me to feel?'

He did not answer that. 'Could you unbutton your shirt?' he asked her. 'I want to listen to your heart.'

What heart? she thought, but she silently obeyed him and he bent to listen, the stethoscope moving over her chest.

'Any headache?' he asked in his casual voice, as though this were an everyday consultation.

'A little.' Her head was thudding, actually, and from the way he looked at her dilated pupils and grey skin no doubt he guessed that.

He asked her some more questions and she answered in a flat calm voice which betrayed nothing.

'Can I ask you something?' she said when he was coiling his stethoscope into his bag.

'Ask away.'

She sensed that he was oddly relieved by that; his

tone had a grateful ring to it. He was a man of sixty, short, broad with a quiet face and observant eyes, and although he had a rather attractive young partner who was a distinctly eligible bachelor, the patients for miles around would always rather have Dr Farmer. He had that authority his young partner lacked. He had seen illness for so many years and could diagnose it in a glance at times.

She hesitated before asking her question because it was going to hurt to ask and even more to hear the answer although she already knew it. She had to hear it, though. It had to be said aloud.

'I lost the baby, didn't I?'

'Yes,' he said gently, and he didn't touch her, but he was watching her closely with sympathy and attention.

She bent her head, her mouth trembling. 'How long is it?'

'Since it happened?' he interpreted gently.

She nodded.

'A year.'

She looked up, shocked. 'A year? That long?'

He smiled at her. 'I'm afraid so.'

'Why?' she asked shakily.

He understood the question. 'The mind has ways of defending itself. You needed to get away, so you went.'

She laughed unevenly. 'You make it sound so simple!'

'It is,' he agreed. 'You hid, Marina. A lot of people want to do it and sometimes they can't find the way, but you did. You just went back in time to a nicer place.'

She wondered how long she would have stayed there if Gideon hadn't come to force her out of it. She remembered now the arguments between him and Grandie, and Gideon saying: 'I know it's a risk, but it's one I've got to take.'

She winced and turned her head away as though that would make the memories leave, but they hung there, heavy as clouds of incense, obscuring her mind.

'There are some tests I want you to take,' the doctor told her. 'You'll have to go into a hospital to have them, I'm afraid.'

She nodded, indifferent to that.

'You don't need to worry.' He was reassuring her because he thought the shadows in her face were caused by worry. 'You had some pretty extensive testing after it first happened. Your concussion left no brain damage. But just in case anything has developed since, I'd like you to have an encephalogram reading. A routine check, nothing more. It would be best to have a thorough check-up at the same time in other departments.'

She nodded again, her eyes on her twisting hands.

'I'll leave you some pills for that headache,' he added. 'How bad is it?'

She sighed. 'Not too bad. Just an ache.'

'Where?' he asked. 'At the front? The temples?'

She nodded, and he laid a cool hand on her brow as though he could feel the pain throbbing there and was testing the strength of it.

'How bad was the accident?' she asked suddenly.

He took his hand away and looked gravely at her. 'No lasting damage was done.'

She laughed at that and his face grew more grave, seeing the wildness in her eyes, the anger.

'You came off quite lightly,' he assured her. 'Nobody walks under a car and gets away scot-free.'

He opened a screwtop jar and took out two pills, shook them into her palm and gave her some water to drink with them. 'I'll leave the pills with your grandfather,' he told her. 'Take two every six hours while you're awake for as long as the headache persists, and if it gets any worse, call me at once. Or if any other symptoms appear—dizziness, sickness, a loss of balance. You don't have any of those?'

All of them, she thought, but not in the sense you mean. Aloud, she said, 'No, I'm fine. Just this headache.'

'Good.' He patted her shoulder. 'You're going to be all right, Marina. Don't fret now.'

He took care of the physical symptoms with the utmost attention, but it was the mental symptoms which could kill.

'I knew it would go away when the time was ripe,' he said with a bland satisfaction as he went.

She lay down on the bed and watched the draining light. It was only a short time since she walked into that room and heard Gideon play, but she had been falling forwards through time and it had been a tiring journey.

She needed to sleep. She wanted to cut everything from her memory. When Grandie came in she sighed, biting her lip. She did not want to talk about it.

He sat down on the edge of the bed and his gnarled stiff fingers took hold of one of her hands and stroked it. She felt the love and anxiety in him and couldn't turn away.

'How do you feel?' he asked her softly.

'Fine,' she said, as she had said to the doctor, and she had lied to both of them, but Grandie looked at her with the suffering face of one who is not deceived and she saw him shrink as though she had hit him.

'I wish to God I'd never let him cross the threshold!' he burst out. 'I knew the moment I set eyes on him with you that this would happen. I warned him, but he's the most ...'

'Don't talk about him,' Marina said harshly, and his bowed fingers squeezed her hand and he groaned under his breath.

'I'd like to sleep now.'

He looked at her and brushed her hair back from her face with a careful hand. 'Of course,' he said, half eager, half concerned. 'You are all right? Would you like me to stay with you? I can sit in the chair and keep as still as a mouse.'

She laughed briefly. 'No, thank you, Grandie. There's no need.'

He did not want to leave her alone, she realised, by the way he looked at her. He was afraid. She sighed and touched his face.

'I am fine, really. I shall just sleep. The doctor gave me some pills.'

'Yes, he told me.' Grandie hesitated. 'A headache, he said. Is it bad?'

'Not any more. I'm just sleepy.'

There was a lot to say, of course. She had been away for a long time and the woman to whom she had come back was a stranger to her. For the past year she had inhabited the mind and body of a girl, half child, and during those months nobody had even hinted at the truth.

Even Mrs Robinson, she thought, and laughed in a wild way, looking at Grandie and seeing him flinch. 'Poor Mrs Robinson, how she must have longed to talk about it! She was brave all those months.'

Grandie frowned. 'She's been very good—they all have. Everyone has been so kind, Marina.'

They had and she shivered. 'I know. I'm grateful, really. It seems so funny to imagine Mrs Robinson with such an exciting story and not to be able to talk about it.' She paused. 'Not to my face, anyway.' Behind her back, of course, the story must have been the topic of gossip for months. What did they think? Did they all know about Gideon and ... She wouldn't think of that. She felt sick now. Her stomach was heaving and she closed her eyes because the room was going round.

'Are you all right?' Grandie asked anxiously, leaning over her.

'Go away,' she said, thinly. 'Please, just go away and let me sleep.'

She loved Grandie, but right now she wanted to be alone, because only when she was alone could she shut out all the memories and just sink into oblivion.

During the night she woke up and the room was pitch dark and the sea sounded like a hoarse animal out in the mist, moaning in wild complaint. She lay, shivering, and heard a movement somewhere in the darkness. She lifted her head, sighing, and asked, 'Grandie?'

There was someone in the chair not too close to the bed. She heard a stir, breathing.

'Grandie?' she asked again.

She knew, of course, before he rose and the long body uncoiled to a height far beyond that of Grandie.

'Get out of my room!' she whispered shakily.

He stood there, not speaking, but she felt him watching her and she hated him. She did not want him anywhere near her. She said again, 'Get out!' but now she said it louder, her voice shrill, and he came towards the bed, his black shadow looming over her like a threat.

'Get out!' she screamed, and the door burst open and Grandie hobbled in panting, exhausted by his race to get there. He looked at Gideon with a hatred little short of hers.

'I told you to stay away from her!'

Gideon didn't speak. He went out, and Grandie came to the bed to look down at her shadowed features on the pillow.

'What did he do?' He sounded so angry that Marina almost smiled.

'Nothing. I woke up and he was sitting there.'

'Damn him!' snarled Grandie, and then he said some other things in a low hoarse mumble, swearing viciously and clenching his hands as though he could kill Gideon.

Gideon had been one of his pupils; Grandie had been very proud of that. He had wanted Gideon to learn to probe beneath the dazzling gloss of his surface technique and when he did Grandie had been delighted. Gideon had developed beyond the master of bravura that he had once been and Grandie had been glowing with pride as he listened to him. Now he hated him for Marina's sake and all his pride in Gideon had gone.

She watched him and wondered for the first time how much Grandie knew. His hatred for Gideon had to have some reason. She looked at him searchingly and asked point-blank, 'How much has he told you?'

Grandie sat down slowly and took both her hands. 'Everything,' he said. 'He didn't hide anything.' He sounded as though he could even hate Gideon for being honest. 'I wanted to kill him at the time. I told him to stay away from you from then on, but of course he didn't. When did Gideon ever do what he was asked? He's self-willed, oblivious to the needs and wishes of everyone else in the world.'

Marina nodded. Closing her eyes, she gave a weary little yawn. 'I'll go back to sleep.'

'Let me stay,' Grandie whispered as though he pleaded, and she smiled at him tenderly.

'For a little while, then, until I'm asleep.'

He patted her hands before he went and sat where Gideon had sat, watching her, and she fell asleep again before long, sinking into a blank world.

She woke up to hear the angry voices down below and to know that Gideon had not gone. Grandie was shouting, but then he lowered his voice to a furious whisper. She could guess what he was saying. Gideon was refusing to go and Grandie was trying to throw him out.

Marina sat up and looked at the two neat dolls. Emma's green ballet shoes stuck up as though she had danced all night. For the past year they had been there, watching her, but now she had grown out of them and she recognised it with regret.

They had been her childhood substitutes for friends and she had left them behind when she met Gideon, although she had kept up the game during the early days. The woman who lay in the bed looked at the bland empty little faces and sighed.

They were lucky, even though they didn't know it. They didn't have to come out of their calm placid little world and face reality.

There were still a lot of things she had to face, lying there in the bed and shivering as though she were cold. She looked back over the few days Gideon had spent at the cottage and realised a lot of things which had passed over her head at the time.

She realised for a start why he had looked so white and shocked when they met, why he had stopped his car and run like a madman as he saw her at the cliff edge. He had thought she might be going to jump off.

That was why he had stared at her, hardly daring to come any closer as she looked back at him. When he realised she just didn't know him he had dared to come closer, but he had been shattered when she smiled at him. She could see his face now, the shocked disbelief in it. It was funny, she thought. Wasn't it funny? She had recognised that he was shocked and had generalised it, wondering if people didn't often smile at him and being surprised by that. Of course he had been taken aback. The last thing he had expected from her was a broad smile.

Gideon was a swine, she thought, realising how he had been moving closer to her every day—touching her, kissing her, charming her all over again, safe behind his anonymous cloak, aware that she had no memory of him to protect her from him.

Grandie had tried to protect her, to stop him, and she herself had come between them, making it clear to Grandie that she wanted Gideon there and that she liked him. Gideon had used her to get himself inside the house. He had played coldly, cunningly, on her lack of awareness, and Grandie had been helpless.

Suddenly she began to shake as another memory invaded her and her whole body began to burn. That dream, she thought, staring at the dolls with fixed stricken eyes.

Dream? Had it been a dream? Or had she gone to him in a sleepwalker's trance and had Gideon taken what she was unknowingly offering him?

She didn't know. The girl she had believed herself to be would never have done such a thing, but the woman she was in reality might have been so awakened by Gideon's kisses and caressing hands that evening that she might have gone in search of the fulfilment her body craved.

She put her hands over her eyes as sickness crawled inside her. She hadn't, had she?

The door opened and Grandie asked anxiously: 'What is it? Are the headaches worse? Shall I ring the doctor?'

She brushed her eyes and lowered her hands slowly. 'No, I'm quite all right.' She took a deep breath. 'Has he gone?'

Grandie looked hesitantly at her and she saw that he was about to lie to her.

'He hasn't, has he?' she asked harshly.

'I wish I could throw him out,' Grandie muttered, enraged by his own bodily weakness. 'I wish I wasn't so old, my hands so useless.' They flexed weakly on his knees as if he would like to get them round Gideon's strong throat. 'He just refuses to go, and I can't make him.'

'I'll see him,' said Marina, making up her mind.

'What?' Grandie looked horrified, staring at her as if she were insane. 'No! Marina ...'

'I'll see him,' she said in a cold, firm voice. 'And then he will go.'

Grandie tried to argue with her, but she just looked at him and in the end he went out, then she sat and waited, staring at the window and seeing the morning light as though it were a darkness without end.

She was going to send Gideon away for ever and although she had no doubts about the wisdom of that it was going to mean a lot of pain for her, now and in the future. But pain was something she had lived with before and she would live with again. Losing Gideon was going to cripple her the way Grandie had been crippled by his hands, the hands which had once given him all the happiness and meaning life had held for him. It was an ironic joke which life played on one—to use the things that meant most in order to wound one in the end.

She heard his steps and listened to them intently because she was never going to hear them again. He ran up the stairs, two at a time, and she felt the eagerness with which he came into the room. He stood at the door and stared at her for a few seconds before he walked over to the bed in that graceful, predatory lope of his and knelt down beside it to take her hands into his own and lift them to his mouth.

'You're leaving now, Gideon,' she said quietly and his black head shot up and the dark eyes stared at her.

Before he could speak she went on in the same even tone, 'I never want to see you again. Go away and don't come back. You can divorce me, or I'll divorce you, I don't mind which, but I want our marriage ended.'

'Listen to me, Marina,' he broke out huskily, and she shook her head, cutting into the words.

'There's nothing for either of us to say.'

'Let me explain,' he began again, and again she interrupted him.

'There's nothing to explain.'

'Isn't there?' He stood up now, towering over her, his face hard. 'Why won't you let me tell you, then?'

'I don't want to listen to any more lies.'

'I've never lied to you!'

She lowered her head. 'No?' The sarcasm lingered on the air for a moment and Gideon shifted his feet restlessly, his body tense.

'No,' he flung back thickly, 'never. What you saw that day was my first meeting with Diana since the day I realised I loved you.'

It was the first time Gideon had ever admitted he loved her, but it gave her no happiness. The moment she had longed for during the months of their marriage, the joy and relief she had imagined she would feel, did not come. She felt nothing but a dead cold misery.

'It makes no difference how many times it happened.' She looked at him directly, her face contemptuous. 'Once was quite enough.'

'Nothing happened,' he said roughly. 'Nothing that you didn't see. Diana kissed me. I wasn't doing the kissing.'

'If I hadn't walked in at that moment it wouldn't have stopped at kissing,' she said with a twist of her lips.

'Listen to me,' Gideon muttered, sinking on to the bed and taking hold of her shoulders. The dark eyes glared into hers. 'You've got to believe me.'

'I shall never believe you.' She met his stare head on, her eyes icy. 'I never want to see you again. It's over.'

She read the flicker of calculation in his eyes. 'No,' he said. She could read so many of the expressions on that hard, dark face and she had no difficulty in interpreting the thoughts moving in his mind now. He was remembering the way she had responded to him over the last few days and a softness stole over his mouth, his eyes gleamed.

'That wasn't the impression I got the other night,' he said huskily and as their eyes held she knew she had not dreamt the passionate lovemaking which had taken place in his bedroom. She had gone to him like an addict to a drug and Gideon had taken her although he knew she was not aware of what she was doing.

She pushed him away violently, turning her head aside to escape the searching movement of the sensual mouth. 'You had no right,' her voice accused angrily.

'I had every right,' Gideon asserted with his face taut and stiff. 'You came because you wanted me as much as I wanted you, will always want you.' He slid his hand along her neck and the strong fingers pushed into her fine silvery hair, playing with it tenderly. 'I've been barely alive this past year, my darling. I've missed you more than I can tell you. That's why I had to come down, although Grandie had asked me to stay away from you while you couldn't remember. I had to see you—even if only from a distance. I've been living on memories.'

'Then you'll be used to it,' she said tartly, and heard him suck in a deep, bitter breath.

'No!' he cried in protest, a deep wrenched sound which told her how moved he was and she was glad, glad because now he would suffer as she had suffered and would suffer in the future. Gideon had fought against the clutch of love, but now its claws were sunk deep into his flesh and the sight made her shiver with pleasure.

'Just go,' she told him. 'I've no further interest in you. It's over.'

Gideon lifted his head slowly, his face changing. A dangerous stillness came into the black eyes. 'Like hell,' he muttered through his stiff lips. 'Ever since I arrived you've been proving over and over again that you belong to me.'

She couldn't deny that. He had walked in here as a stranger and from the moment he arrived she had been falling in love with him all over again, and she couldn't hide that from him. She had been safe in her dream world, but from that safety she had loved him exactly as she had before and did now. No instinctive blind warning had reached her. She had looked at him and although she sensed that peculiar, troubling familiarity, she had still loved him, moved into his arms without a shadow of doubt.

'You tricked me,' she accused him furiously. 'You took advantage of the fact that I didn't remember.'

'If you really hated me you would never have turned to me again,' he contradicted. 'Underneath the hurt you're feeling you still care.' He smiled at her, his mouth crooked. 'You've had a bad time, darling, and it was all over nothing. Diana never meant a thing to me. I enjoyed her company and her body but I never gave a twopenny damn for her.'

She winced. 'You think that excuses you?'

'No, of course not,' he said impatiently. 'Before I met you that was all women meant to me—a little pleasure when I was tired and needed relaxation. Diana was the perfect lover for a man who didn't want to get involved. With her it was just the same. We used each other's bodies but had no use for each other's hearts.'

Marina did not believe that. She remembered the woman's angry, passionate movements when she and Gideon argued in the road the other day. Even safely protected from her knowledge of what they had been to each other, Marina had picked up those emotions from a distance. Diana loved him even if he did not love Diana.

Gideon bent suddenly and she felt his lips shaking as he kissed her throat. 'She kissed me, darling, I swear it. I didn't kiss her. When you walked in I was shattered by the look on your face.' He groaned deeply, shivering as though he were suddenly ice cold. 'When I ran out into the street and saw you in the road, the blood, the way you lay there so still and silent, I thought . . .' He broke off, gasping, and his arms went round her, held her so tightly she couldn't breath. 'I thought, God help me, you were dead, and I couldn't move. I stood there and I wanted to die too.' He kissed her hair, her cheek, her ear, trying to reach her mouth and being evaded by the turn of her head, her shake of denial.

'Marina,' he whispered, 'I love you. I never even knew how much until I saw you lying in the road and I thought you were dead and I could never tell you.'

'You must go now,' she said coolly, sitting stiffly in the circle of his arms.

He drew back and his eyes flashed. 'Don't do this. I need you.'

'Well, I don't need you,' she snapped, hating him for the way he phrased that because whether he knew it or not he still did not know how to love. He was still putting his own needs in front of everything else. 'You're the last thing I need,' she told him. 'I need you like I need a hole in the head.'

She was totally white, her face clenched in self-control which was going to weaken if he didn't go soon because she wanted to throw herself down on the bed and cry, but if she did, Gideon would take her into his arms and, weakened, she might never have the strength to send him away again.

Gideon stared at her and stood up. The long, lean body stiffened. She met the black probe of his eyes and fought with every ounce of self-control to keep her own gaze level and cold.

'I love you,' he said at last.

'You're too late.' Her lips twisted ironically as she said that. 'Goodbye, Gideon.'

For a long moment he stared at her. Then he turned and walked out of the room. Marina lay down because she was trembling and her head was pounding violently. She closed her eyes and let the world slip far away from her where it couldn't hurt her for a little while.

The sunshine slid around the room like a curious ghost until it found the spilled silvery hair and played with it, giving a reflected brightness to the pale still face. She was sleeping but the tears were crawling down her face and her lips were mumbling silently in her sleep.

CHAPTER SEVEN

WHEN she woke up again the room was filled with the reflections of the dying sun and the house was silent. She shivered, as though she were dying of cold, listening to the emptiness around her. Gideon had gone, she thought, leaving her aching for him, despite her hatred and anger. She slid out of the bed and padded quietly to the window. The gulls floated silently across the sea, streaming behind a returning fishing boat, in a coloured tail of light shed from the setting sun. The fish refuse from the boat would have been thrown over the side, giving the gulls an easy banquet. It was a common sight in the evenings, a fishing boat with a flock of gulls following it.

What was she going to do? She leaned her elbows on the windowsill and tried to think, but it was hard to force her mind to function when her stupid emotions clamoured as they were doing, thrusting pain on to her when she had had enough of it and wanted nothing but peace.

She would have to make a decision about her future. The dreamy romanticism which had sheltered her during these past months had evaporated in the blinding light of memory and now she knew with a pang that the life of the concert artist was not for her. She did not want to travel around the world, as Gideon did, playing at that pitch all the time, always in the public eye, always walking the tightrope of success with no safety net beneath one to cushion one's fall.

Her marriage to Gideon had taught her that much. She did not have the stomach for that life. For her, music was a private, personal thing. The harsh glare of the concert hall distracted her from that intense experience which music gave her when she was alone.

She would have to tell Grandie, but she could not face it yet. She needed a little time in which she could grow some sort of armour before she faced the outside world. It was not going to be easy, but Marina meant to harden herself.

She went to the bathroom and washed, paused to listen for some sound downstairs and heard nothing. Grandie had perhaps gone for a walk. She dressed and went downstairs, but when she walked into the kitchen she stopped dead, two little coins of red beginning to burn in her cheeks.

Gideon looked at her coolly. 'Coffee?'

'What are you still doing here?' She was breathless and angry, her eyes dark.

He didn't answer that. Pouring some coffee, he pushed the cup across the table. Ruffy came out from a corner and leapt up at her. Absently she patted the dog's rough white coat, her eyes still fixed on Gideon and words churning uselessly around her head.

'Where's Grandie?'

'Playing chess with the vicar,' he said in a normal conversational tone. 'You must be hungry. What would you like to eat?'

'Does Grandie know you're still here?'

Gideon looked at her without answering, his expression mild and slightly sardonic.

It had been a stupid question. Of course Grandie must know he was still here! Why had Grandie gone out, leaving him alone in the house with her? Gideon had always been able to make other people do as he wished, turning the magnet of his willpower on them and coercing them without difficulty. She had thought that Grandie hated him as much as she did, that he would fight Gideon's will, but Grandie had gone out and left her undefended.

Gideon was watching her, reading her thoughts, the black eyes glittering with a mockery which lay along the hard curve of his mouth too, telling her that her rebellious stare was amusing him.

'Yes,' he said softly, 'Grandie has abandoned you to me. This is one battle you're going to have to fight all by yourself, Marina.'

'Don't think I can't,' she retorted fiercely, her chin raised in defiance. 'I told you to go and I meant every word of it. I don't want you here.' She took a short sharp breath. 'I don't want you,' she emphasised.

His dark eyes took on a cool glimmer which did not betray his thoughts. 'What do you want to eat?' he asked again. 'It will have to be something simple. I'm no great cook, but I can do you anything with eggs—boiled, fried or scrambled.'

'I'm not hungry,' she told him shortly.

His glance was derisive. He moved to the stove and began to make scrambled eggs while she watched him, seething.

'Drink your coffee!' He spoke over his shoulder without looking at her.

Marina sat down at the table and drank the coffee slowly. Gideon turned and placed the scrambled eggs and toast in front of her. 'More coffee?' He did not wait for her to answer but took her cup and poured some coffee for both of them before he sat down opposite her.

'What are you doing here?' She could barely taste the food; her mind would not adapt to the ordinary functions of life. She was too much on edge, her stomach churning. 'I told you, I don't ever want to see you again.'

'I know what you told me.' He sounded indif-

ferent and that infuriated her. He sat there, totally
at ease, those long legs stretched out casually, his
body lounging in the chair, a dark green sweater
covering his deep chest, the rollneck ruffled where
his dark hair brushed against it, his face expression-
less beneath the rough tangle of those black curls.
He looked as though he had been walking out in the
wind, his skin glowing from long struggles with the
elements. Marina ran her eyes over him with dislike.

'Get out and don't come back!'

'Eat your eggs.' He was taking no notice of anything she said and her hands clenched at her sides.
She wanted to pick up her coffee and throw it at
him.

'Go back to Diana!' she flung, and at once wished
she had not mentioned that name because the black
glitter of his eyes filled with amusement and a sort
of satisfaction, and she knew she had betrayed something of her own inner turmoil, her confused
emotions. She wanted him to believe that she was
certain and clear about what she wanted, and that
stupid slip had told him she wasn't.

She got up, and Ruffy lifted his ears alertly, obviously hoping she intended to take a walk. 'Get
out!' She stared at Gideon as she shouted the words,
but his manner did not change.

'I'm not going anywhere.' He leaned back in his
chair, his hands linked behind that black head, giving an elegant and powerful line to his long body
which she wished she did not instinctively catch herself noticing. She did not want to notice him, to feel
the desire he could arouse throbbing away in her

own body. 'I'm staying right here,' Gideon ended coolly, smiling faintly.

'How can you be such a swine?' Her voice shook as she demanded that and he smiled tormentingly.

'I work at it.'

He had no sense of shame. He had betrayed her with that woman. She wouldn't be surprised if he had done so throughout their marriage. Now he was forcing her to accept his company and angrily she had to recognise that there was no way in which she could force him to go. Gideon had always been strong-willed, assertive. She stood there, staring at him with hostility, trembling.

'Your eggs will get cold,' he said.

She looked at the food and felt nausea, but if she ran away now she would convince him that she was still vulnerable, still wide open to him. Slowly she sat down again and began to eat, forcing the food into her mouth although she felt sick. How dared he sit there like that, mocking her, laughing at her, those dark eyes filled with wicked amusement? After all he had done to her, he felt he could still charm her back into his arms.

He had reason for his optimism, of course. During her lost months, her desire for him hadn't faded. As soon as he came back into her life Gideon had realised that he still attracted her. That night when he had deliberately caressed her and aroused her, it had been she who had gone to him, not the other way around. Gideon had known very well what he was doing as he held her on his lap and fondled her, kissed her in that coaxing, passionate way. He had reached into her subconscious to re-awaken her desire for him and he had succeeded. She had sleep-walked to him because at that hidden level of her mind she had known precisely what she wanted.

Was it any wonder that now he refused to go? Without knowing what she was doing she had betrayed that sleeping passion to him. She finished her unwanted food and drank the last of the coffee.

'I'm going to bed,' she said coldly, and stood up.

'Goodnight,' Gideon returned with a taunting little smile.

She eyed him with a deep desire to hit him, her hands taut at her sides. He grinned as he took in the expression on her face and the long body uncoiled. He stood up and she almost ran to the door, hearing him laughing behind her as she banged out of the room.

She bolted her bedroom door, but there was no need; Gideon did not follow her. Undressing again, she slipped into the bed. The dolls sat in their accustomed places and she stared at them, and now they were just dolls. She had been a late developer; a child when she met Gideon, a child when he seduced her, a child when she carried his child inside her body.

No wonder she had fled back to her safe, halcyon existence when the problems of adulthood grew too great. She had been too young both in age and in attitude to cope with Gideon. He must have known that.

Grandie had kept her in this house like a doll in a glass case—like Snow White in her perfect sleep, cherished and petted and eternally a child. Grandie had loved her, but he had been forcing her to accept the role he planned for her, forcing his own ambitions on her from her earliest years, shaping her, forming her in his own image. Although she loved music and was happy to work hard at it, she had always lacked Grandie's drive to the peak of achievement. She had accepted the role forced on her at such an early age, but she had never really desired it. She had loved her quiet backwater at Basslea. She had loved her music. But the world into which Grandie had planned to force her had never been the world she wanted.

It was something she had slowly come to recognise at college. She had ability—she did not doubt that. She could work and learn. But she did not have the real drive which carried men like Gideon upward. She was not in his class.

He had said that to her and she had blithely taken it to mean that she was his superior, but all the time Gideon had meant the opposite.

Now she faced that and knew Gideon was right. For all the hard gloss he had once used to cover his lack of inner feeling, Gideon was still one of the most brilliant pianists of his age, and since he had gained a new ability to interpret the music with passion and understanding, no doubt he would climb even higher. She had seen the beginning of that climb during their marriage.

Slowly she fell asleep, and in the morning she picked up Meg and Emma and smiled at them before she put them away on the top shelf of her wardrobe. One day some other little girl would play with them. It would not be her. They had been her companions in a lonely world which she no longer inhabited.

Dressed in blue jeans and a brief blue T-shirt, she went down and found Gideon cooking tomatoes and bacon. He glanced sideways at her and she met his eyes with a cool and level stare.

'Why haven't you gone?' she demanded.

'Breakfast is ready,' he said as if she hadn't spoken. Marina saw that that was how he meant to play it, ignoring her requests for him to go, impervious to her hostility and anger.

'I meant what I said. Our marriage is over.'

'It hasn't even started. Pour the coffee.'

'Where's Grandie now?' Although she asked the question irritably she was pouring coffee and sitting down. Sunshine streamed into the room and Ruffy sniffed hungrily, his tail wagging as he contemplated the prospect of delicious bacon rinds in a minute.

'You wait for it,' Gideon told him, placing the plate in front of her. Seating himself opposite, he eyed his own breakfast hungrily. 'I'm ravenous—I don't know about you.' He glanced up. 'Grandie has walked down to the village.'

Marina looked back at him in surprise. 'Gone to the village?'

'Why shouldn't he?' Gideon bent over his plate and ate with obvious enjoyment. His shirt lay open at the collar, revealing the strong line of his brown throat and the first scattering of dark hairs on the deep chest. A wave of black hair fell along his cheek and she had to fight down an impulse to push it back into place. She dared not touch him.

Grandie went to the village every day, of course,

to shop and chat to people, but it surprised her that he should go out this morning, leaving her alone with Gideon again. Grandie admired success. Gideon had been one of his most successful pupils and he had been proud of him.

Looking up, Gideon caught her eye and said mockingly, 'Close your mouth. Are you catching flies? Eat your breakfast—it's delicious. I'm becoming a very good cook.' He knew very well why she was looking so taken aback and it amused him. The gleam in the black eyes made her so angry she stiffened and snapped forcefully:

'Why don't you go where you're wanted? I don't want you here.'

'Too bad,' he shrugged, and bent over his meal again.

After a furious pause Marina ate her own breakfast and found that this morning the smell of food did not make her nauseated. She was hungry and she finished the meal without another word. Gideon cut up the bacon rinds and fed them to Ruffy, who wagged his tail as he watched. Gideon scratched his head and Marina watched the long fingers moving seductively on the dog's white coat with a dryness in her throat.

Gideon looked up and she felt her face burn. Hurriedly she turned away and began to clear the table.

If she stayed here with him always around she was going to be fighting a losing battle—she faced that angrily. Gideon moved beside her, out of the line of her vision, and her blood responded to every beat of his heart, every breath he took.

She made herself continue doing the washing up

although she was aware of everything he did, every move he made. When she had finally finished she turned to walk to the door and Gideon stepped in front of her; not touching her, just barring her way, smiling down at her with those straight black brows lifting in mocking amusement.

'Get out of my way,' she said hoarsely.

'Make me.' He said that with enjoyment, his eyes alight.

She put her hands against his chest to push him away, but that was a mistake, because she felt the trembling start inside her as soon as she touched him, and she had to snatch her hands away because of what they might do, the weakness they might unveil too clearly for him.

Looking away from his observant stare she said thickly: 'How can you do this? Go back to your mistress, I don't want you.'

'I haven't got a mistress, and you do want me,' he said very softly, watching her.

She lifted her head to look at him furiously. 'Is the affair with Diana over? How sad. I'm sure you'll find someone else.'

'I'm sure I could,' he agreed casually, and that deepened her rage with him. His complacent smile made her want to hit him.

'It won't be me,' she snapped.

'No?' He put his head to one side and ran an exploratory eye over her from the bright tip of her head to her feet, taking his time, making his enjoyment only too clear. 'Didn't you enjoy being my mistress, Marina?'

She felt red colour rush up her face. She hit him

so hard it made her hand sting. For a second Gideon looked at her with rage, his black eyes obsidian, furious, then he took her by the shoulders and bent her backwards, despite her helpless struggles. She turned her head away to avoid the searching mouth and felt it moving along her exposed neck. Her trembling increased and with it so did her anger.

'Let me go, you swine!' she cried harshly.

Without answering, Gideon caught her chin in one hand, his fingers biting into her, turning her face up towards him, then his lips were heatedly opening her own and the ground under her feet seemed to shake. Fire streaked along her nerves. Her eyes shut tight. She felt her body arch towards him and then his hands ran sensuously over her back, pressing her body closer, the stroking caress of their movements wiping out all memory inside her.

Her small hands moved up to clutch at his shirt and the reality of his body under her fingers made the blood sing in her veins. No pleasure her hands had ever had from their skill on the piano could equal the piercing sweetness she felt as she slid her hands up Gideon's body, deeply aware of the muscular hardness of the flesh and sinew beneath her fingertips.

Her response had speeded up the hammering beat of his heart. His hands moved up under her T-shirt, their cool exploration running up her bare back to close possessively over her small breasts.

Harshness enveloped her and she abruptly dragged herself away, breathing heavily.

'Get your hands off me!'

His face was darkly flushed, his eyes glittering.

'You want my hands on you,' he muttered thickly, his speech slurred by the pressure of the desire she could read in his intent stare. His eyes closed and opened again, fierceness in them. 'Don't you know what you do to me?'

'Any woman can do that,' she said savagely, and saw his face whiten.

'No,' he said unsteadily. 'Nobody else.'

'Is that what you told Diana?' She gave him a cold, bitter little smile. 'You do it so well, Gideon, a well-rehearsed patter you must have delivered many times before, but this time it isn't going to work. I don't believe a word of it.'

'It's true,' he broke out with his black eyes fixed on her, a burning intensity in them. 'I love you. With Diana, with everyone else, it was just pleasure—none of them ever made my heart stop the way you do, the way you did the first time I ever set eyes on you.'

Her eyes widened—she remembered that night, the concert, the party, the adoring women thronging around him and hanging on his every word, the black flash of his eyes as he noticed her and the way he held her hand later, smiling down at her with reckless, excited eyes.

'You were such a baby,' he said in a husky, shaken voice. 'Big innocent eyes and a shy little smile—my God, I wanted you the moment I saw you.'

Marina remembered all too well the gleaming brilliance of those eyes as they stared at her. Was that what he had been thinking? Had there been desire behind those hard black eyes? He had stood there, tall and elegant in his evening clothes, looking at her with exalted amusement, and she had imagined his excitement came from his triumph during the performance. She had barely dared to lift her head to look at him; the magician whose powerful hands had made that wonderful music. She had certainly not suspected that while Gideon stared down at her, he had had thoughts like that in his head. It would never have entered her mind. He was right. She had been innocent, naïve, unaware of all the sexual complications which Gideon was to teach her.

'A mistress was all you ever wanted, wasn't it?' she accused, her eyes bitter as she raised them to his face again.

He read the contempt she was showing him and his mouth twisted wryly as he shrugged those broad shoulders in acceptance of the charge. 'Have you ever seen it from my side of things, Marina? You've met my mother, you know what she's like. From an early age I got dragged around the world like a performing monkey, given everything I ever wanted, but always treated more as a toy than a child. My mother suffocated me. I never had a free hour to myself. I wasn't allowed to breathe unless she gave me permission. I had no friends because she didn't want me to be distracted from my music. My father was shoved aside because he might interfere between me and my mother.'

She knew all this, had worked it out for herself from what she had observed of his mother and from what Grandie had told her.

Gideon grimaced, his features set hard in grim disillusionment. 'When I could break away, I did, and I determined then that I would never again get seriously involved with another woman during my lifetime.' His eyes flashed as he stared over her head. 'If you let them, women take you over completely —that's what I learnt from my mother. They stifle you, smother you, cling round you like ivy. I decided when I grew up that women had their uses but they had to be firmly kept in their place. I learnt to use them, enjoy them and then kick them out of my life when I'd finished with them.'

She winced at the harsh cruelty of that and he watched her face, his own shadowed. 'Yes,' he agreed, 'it isn't pretty. I could lie to you and hide all of that, but I don't want any more secrets between us, Marina. I want you to know what I am, what I've been.'

There was a grinding ache in the centre of her body, a pain which was as persistent as toothache and far more destructive. She thought she might have it for the rest of her life.

'I don't want to hear any more,' she said in a flat dry voice. She pulled away from him and turned to the door, but Gideon caught her arm and held her back, his dark eyes fixed on her.

'Marina,' he muttered huskily, and she flared up in anger.

'Why don't you leave me alone? I've had enough of you—I hate the sight of you. Go away and stay away!'

The sharpness of her voice slashed across his face like a whip and his hand dropped away from her. She caught a glimpse of the pain in his eyes as she stumbled to the door, but she did not care. She hoped she had hurt him; it would be a small revenge for all the agony he had given her in the past.

She met Grandie as she wandered along the cliff. His bowed figure halted as he set eyes on her and she felt him search her face for some sign which would tell him how she was reacting to Gideon's continued presence.

'He asked me to give him a chance to talk to you,' he told her anxiously. 'Did I do wrong? I couldn't make him go—he just ignored everything I said.'

'I realise that,' she said flatly. Gideon was obstinate, self-willed, impossible to move when he had set his mind on something.

'What's happening?' Grandie asked, watching her. 'Is he staying? What are you going to do?'

'I don't know,' she muttered, her head bent. She had to tell him some time; it might as well be now. Taking a deep breath, she said unsteadily, 'I can't ever be what you want me to be, Grandie. It isn't in me.'

He stiffened, his hands curling in that useless clawlike way at his side. 'You're brilliant,' he burst out. 'You could be a top artist. If you hadn't met Gideon you would have begun to show what you could do.'

She shook her head sadly. 'It isn't Gideon.'

'Yes,' Grandie said furiously. 'Gideon ruined your career, your whole life.'

'My life, maybe,' she sighed, 'not my career. Sooner or later I'd have had to tell you what I'm telling you now—I'm not cut out for it.'

'How can you say that?'

She lifted her pale gleaming head and looked at

him with reluctant, sad eyes. 'It's the truth, Grandie, whether you'll admit it or not. I haven't got the nerve for the heights. I'd never succeed because I lack whatever it is that drives Gideon and drove you once. I don't even want to become a great concert artist. I hate playing in public, it makes me sick. I love music, but I hate performing, I hate people listening to me.'

'You haven't even tried yet,' Grandie said fiercely, staring at her as if he wished he could shake some sense into her. 'How do you know how you'd feel once you'd started? We all feel stage fright. We're all aware of being inadequate. Once you start playing you'd soon get over that.'

She shook her head. 'That isn't it, Grandie. Don't you see? I don't want to do it.'

Grandie wanted her to be a clone of himself; an imitation which could give him the chance to relive his own life, the life he had had snatched away from him by a cruel fate. Grandie had never ceased to resent the loss of his ability. He had been excluded from a world he longed for and he could not believe that Marina could turn her back on that world without a single regret.

'We aren't all the same, Grandie,' she told him gently. 'I'm sorry if I'm disappointing you . . .'

'Disappointing me?' His face was harsh and his eyes shadowed. 'I've given my every waking thought to you since you were born. How can you turn your back on what I know you could be? How can you throw it all away, Marina? You're brilliant. You have a sensitive touch, a great understanding and feeling for the music. Why waste all that ability?

What are you going to do with it?' His face tightened. 'You're going back to him, after all he's done to you! Don't women ever learn? Gideon is selfish —all great artists are. I don't blame him for that. He lives at a terrific pace and he needs to be able to relax and wind down between performances. I wouldn't care what he did, but if he comes between you and your career again I'll never forgive him!'

'It has nothing to do with Gideon,' she said again.

'I'm not blind,' Grandie snapped furiously. 'As soon as he appeared down here you started falling for him all over again. Do you think I don't know what was going on between you?' His face was red, his eyes bitter. 'That night I came in and found you in his arms I could see how far he'd got.'

'He's nothing to do with it,' she repeated on a rising note. She did not want to think about Gideon, let alone talk about him.

Pushing past Grandie, she ran down the cliff path and turned into the way which led to Spanish Headland. The wind whipped her hair into tangles and brought a bright colour to her cheeks which gave a deceptive glow to her small face.

She stood on the sheep-cropped turf and stared out across the sea. Below those blue sun-glinting waves lay savage rocks which could rend and destroy any boat foolish enough to venture into these waters. People could be as deceptive as this—she had had a chart to warn her against Gideon from the start, but she had come to grief, all the same, because she had not taken the warning messages of her intuition seriously.

Although she had been so very young she had not

been blinded by Gideon's looks and charm. She had realised that he was hard, a man used to getting what he wanted, a man with few illusions and a cynical desire for his own way. Passion had undermined her realisation of his nature. It had taken the bitter lessons which pain could teach to show her that for every hour of pleasure in his arms she would have to pay heavily later.

A woman like Diana Grenoby could match Gideon because she had as little heart as he did, but Marina had no intention of letting his desire for her lure her back to him. Gideon had told her frankly what the future would hold for her one day. He used women and then kicked them out of his life when he was tired of them. She wasn't going to have that happen to her. He had already hurt her as much as she could stand.

She believed he imagined he loved her for the moment. Even Gideon must have been affected by the bitter events of that day when she walked in and found Diana in his arms. She had lost her baby and been seriously ill for a long time. Gideon was not totally hard. He would have been guilty, disturbed. Maybe he had some idea of making reparation for all that had happened. Whatever his reason for telling her he loved her, she would not, could not take it seriously. Gideon did not know what love meant.

CHAPTER EIGHT

MARINA heard a grating step behind her and swung,
her pale face filled with immediate defiance, expecting to see Gideon. The young man behind her
looked at her uncertainly, his fair skin flushing. 'Oh,
hello,' he muttered, not quite meeting her eyes.

'Hallo,' she said, relaxing. 'You haven't gone back
to Birmingham yet, then?'

Tom Hutton shook his head, turning from her to
look out across the sea in his turn.

'Still staying in the village?' Marina asked.

He nodded, then cleared his throat in an endear-
ingly embarrassed fashion. 'Sorry I mistook your
friend for your father the other day.'

She remembered Gideon's deliberate kiss, timed
for Tom Hutton to witness, the hesitation with
which Gideon had tried to find a way of making her
stay away from him. She could have laughed if she
had not been so angry with him. He had been
trapped, unable to say openly why he objected to
her friendly meeting with Tom. So, being Gideon,
he had attempted to put a stop to any relationship
by kissing her so that Tom should see it.

She smiled at Tom. 'That's all right. He is much
older than me.'

He glanced at her in that uncertain way. 'I thought he was,' he agreed.

Marina sensed that he had not heard any gossip in the village about her. The people there might love to gossip, but only among themselves. Faced with a stranger, they closed ranks. Tom would not have picked up any of the truth about her from them.

They had been splendid during her long amnesia. She had never got so much as a hint from them that everything was not normal. She looked back over the days of Gideon's visit, though, and picked up a dozen little moments when they had come close to betraying something of the secret. They had all known that Gideon was her husband, of course, they had met him during his visits here in the past. Yet they had carefully avoided giving away their knowledge of him except when their tongues slipped. She had known that there was something odd about Gideon. It had never occurred to her that there was something odd about her.

Tom moved closer, staring at her averted, serious face. 'Are you engaged to him or something?'

Marina smiled drily. 'Something,' she said, not wishing to go into all the details.

The fair young face sobered again. 'Oh, I see,' he muttered with a slight shrug, and it was something of a comfort to see disappointment in his eyes as he half turned to walk away.

'Seen any good birds lately?' she asked, half-teasingly.

He laughed, gesturing to the binoculars round his neck. 'A few. I saw a goldfinch as I came along through the village, and yesterday I caught a glimpse of a heron over the river.'

'You wouldn't need binoculars to see that,' she smiled.

'No,' he agreed. 'Quite unmistakable.'

'There's a heronry two miles from here,' she told him. 'If you go to Bindley you'll probably see several of them.'

'I must remember that,' said Tom, his manner warming. 'I like watching the waders when the tide is out. They look so funny digging in the sand.'

'Like busy waiters hurrying about,' she agreed, laughing.

'You're lucky, living here,' he sighed. 'You must see so much.'

'I was born here. You get used to seeing the sea and all the birds. You take it for granted. I think people who only come here once a year from the town get a lot more out of it than we do.'

'I often think I'll try to get a job in the country,' Tom said. 'The pay wouldn't be so good, but I'd get a lot more out of life than I do now.'

'If you don't like town life you'd be mad to stay there,' she nodded, turning to go.

He fell into step beside her. 'Is your friend still here? Does he live here?'

She glanced at him and away. 'He's still here,' she admitted.

'Oh.' Tom was silent for a moment, walking beside her with his head bent. 'Pity,' he muttered, and gave her a quick look to catch her reaction to that.

Marina smiled at him. 'Thank you.' Her tone did not encourage him to go on, although it was friendly and polite, and with someone like Tom one did not have to be brutal in order to get a message home.

They had reached the cottage and Marina halted in her tracks, turning to smile her goodbye at him. 'I hope you enjoy the rest of your stay,' she said.

Ruefully Tom smiled back at her. 'It's been nice meeting you again,' he offered, and then they both heard the front door open.

Gideon walked down the path, a harsh frown drawing his brows together. Tom shot him a quick look and took in the poised menace of that face before he nodded hurriedly at Marina and walked away fast without looking towards Gideon again.

She turned and the dark eyes searched her face, probing the cool, remote expression she showed him. 'He's still hanging around, is he?'

Marina faced him coldly. She saw the jealous darkness in his eyes, but she refused to care. He had no business looking at her like that, his glance narrowed and hard.

'Stay away from him,' Gideon broke out.

'Would you get out of my way, please?' She moved towards the gate, but he still blocked her path, his hands at his sides but his fingers curled into fists.

'If you're trying to annoy me, take my advice,' he said tersely, through tightened lips. 'Don't.'

'Why should I want to annoy you?' Marina let her eyes drift over him in icy rejection. 'Who I talk to is my business.'

'You're my wife, whether you like it or not,' Gideon told her, the hardness increasing in his face.

'I don't like it, and the sooner it ceases to be true,

the better I shall be pleased. I want a divorce and I want it quickly.'

He brushed that aside, concentrating on the subject engrossing him at the moment. 'Don't try to change the subject. Stay away from that boy. I won't have him looking at you the way he does.'

'Don't judge everyone by your own standards! Tom's a very nice young man.'

Gideon's eyes flared. 'And he wouldn't want to do anything but look, I suppose?' Cynicism twisted his mouth. 'I don't buy that. Sooner or later he'd want a lot more than that.'

'Maybe when I've got rid of you I'll find out,' she told him with acid in her voice.

A snarl came into his voice. 'Don't push me too far!'

Her temper rose to meet his and her face flushed darkly. 'Who do you think you are? How dare you come stamping down the path just because I'm passing the time of day with a friendly young man?'

His eyes were glittering like black steel. 'Friendly? Is that how you'd describe it? He fancies you and you know it.'

'What if he does? That's no business of yours.'

'Like hell it isn't!' He grabbed her arm and she wrenched it out of his grasp, glaring at him.

'Keep your hands off me!'

'You're not to see him again, do you hear?' Gideon was in an explosive mood now, his whole body as tense as a violin string.

Marina saw Grandie hovering at the window, anxiety in the way he peered at them. 'Let me pass,' she insisted.

He drew a harsh, impeded breath, but at last he moved aside and she walked past him into the cottage. Grandie hobbled to meet her. 'What's wrong?' he asked, staring at her.

Gideon loomed up behind her, his eyes contemptuous. 'She's not a child any more, Grandie. Leave it.'

His arrogance put a match to Grandie's smouldering temper. 'She doesn't want you here and neither do I,' he burst out hoarsely. 'You've done enough to both of us, Gideon. Get out of this house and out of our lives!'

Gideon's eyes were filled with that impassive opaque blankness which he could assume as a cloak when he was pursuing some course of action which others were trying to impede. He eyed Grandie and said nothing, his face immovable. Grandie stared at him, clenched and shaking, before he turned and stamped up the stairs.

'Have you ever thought of anything but yourself?' Marina asked Gideon bitterly, walking away from him into the kitchen. The air was filled with the fragrance of freshly prepared salad. A large bowl of it stood on the kitchen table, which was laid for lunch for three.

Gideon came up behind her as she stared at it. His voice spoke just at her ear, soft, smooth, intimate. 'I think of you, all the time. You know that.'

'Liar,' she said, not turning to look at him, but aware in every fibre of her being of the lean hard body just behind her.

'It's the truth. Do you know the old legend about a man who went to sleep under an olive tree and a scorpion crawled into his ear and ate its way into his brain? That's what you did to me.' He sounded as though he were mocking her, his voice amused.

'If I were a scorpion I'd sting you to death.'

He laughed, running a finger down the centre of her spine, making her tingle with nervous electricity. 'Vixen.'

'Grandie asked you to go. Why don't you?'

'You know why,' he murmured, kissing her arm.

Marina tugged it away irritably. Every touch made her head spin and she knew she had a very low resistance to Gideon's insidious lovemaking. She would despise herself if she gave way. She had to hang on to the things she knew about him, his arrogant use of women in the past, his admission that when he was tired of them he pushed them away with a cold shrug.

He lounged beside her, arms folded, staring at her, and she refused to look at him, although without so much as glancing in his direction she was very well aware of him. Just outside the angle of her vision the dark head moved invitingly, drawing her, but she fought the depth of her own attraction to him.

'Where did you walk? Where did you meet that boy?'

Gideon had a note in his voice which she was beginning to recognise. He was very aware of the difference in their ages, she realised, and resentful of it. He tried to put contempt and mockery into his voice whenever he used that phrase. He had always referred to Paul as 'that boy', she remembered.

Deliberately she turned and glanced at him.

'Tom is hardly a boy. I'd say he was around my own age.'

'He looks about eighteen,' Gideon spat, his face hardening.

Keeping her eyes on his face, watching him closely, she said softly, 'Don't be absurd. You're just fifteen years older than him, that's all.'

His skin took on a dark red heat. After a pause during which she could see him fighting with his temper, he said thickly: 'Very funny.'

'I wasn't being funny.' She opened her eyes wide, all innocence, and he glared at her.

'No,' he said, 'you weren't.' There was another pause, then he moved closer and said huskily, 'Don't tease me, Marina. Don't you know how much I need you?'

'Need me?' She looked at him icily. 'Until the day you've had all you want from me and I get kicked out of your life like all the others, Gideon?'

'No, it isn't like that with you,' he protested. 'With you it was different almost from the start.'

'Was it?' she asked contemptuously. 'You told me yourself that when we met you wanted me, and we both know you didn't have marriage in mind, don't we?'

He flinched. 'No,' he admitted harshly. 'No. One look and I was burning for you and it never even entered my head to marry you.' He saw the anger in her face and said unsteadily, 'Darling, I'm being honest. At least do me the favour of listening to the whole thing. I can't deny the way it started and I don't want to hide anything from you, but it soon changed, Marina. Believe me.'

'Why should I believe a word you say? You've admitted to being a liar and an opportunist.'

'I'm not lying now,' he insisted. 'I admit I came down here in pursuit of you, meaning to seduce you, but that day changed everything.'

She shivered, remembering that clear, frosty winter day, her own excitement at seeing him, the way he smiled at her and said: 'Hello, Red Riding Hood, I'm the wolf.' How funny he must have thought that was—a hidden irony which he would have believed she could not glimpse. She had been so blindly innocent, a child walking into danger without even knowing it. Gideon had teased her, stroked her palm with his finger, kissed her lightly. He had been stealing up on her without haste, a stealthy predator whose intentions were hidden from her.

He felt her anger and moved restlessly, touching her arm. 'But I didn't go on with it, darling. I couldn't. Because while I was here you played to me and while I listened I suddenly saw what you were and I hated myself. You were a creature from a world I'd never known existed. You played with such sensitivity and sweetness, a beautiful tranquillity. I listened and I hated myself. I walked out of here that day never meaning to see you again. I knew I had no right to touch you, any more than I would have a right to crush a flower.'

He moved closer to her and she suddenly heard the unsteady beating of his heart just behind her back.

'When I was back in London I told myself I'd

been a fool, but I couldn't forget you. You kept coming into my head.'

She was listening now, intently, her face pale. Gideon sighed and put his cheek on her shoulder.

'But then I met you again in London and I knew I had to see you. I wanted to find out more about you, discover if you really were as gentle and innocent as you seemed. But I never laid a hand on you —you can't say I did, Marina. I was very careful with you. I never saw you alone, never took you to my flat, never said a word to you that couldn't have been heard by anyone else.'

She had to believe that, remembering how they had always met in public places where they were under observation all the time. Gideon had taken her to restaurants, theatres, parks, but he had never taken her to his flat and he had never made any attempt to touch her. It had not occurred to her that he had been deliberately staying out of temptation.

'I was afraid of being alone with you,' he muttered harshly. 'I knew that if I had the chance I'd give in to temptation. The more I got to know you the more it mattered to me that you should stay as sweet and untouched as you were. The life I'd led had made me the wrong man for you. Do you think I didn't know that?'

'Then why did you go on seeing me?' she asked, angry because he did not seem to realise that he had been wounding her during those months, the months when he had come and gone like the swallow and she had never known if he cared twopence for her.

'I couldn't stop,' he admitted on a mutter of pain.

'While I was going round the world I found myself thinking about you all the time. You were in my head and then in my blood, and then I realised you were necessary to me. I'd sworn that I'd never again let another woman take over my life, but without even knowing what you were doing, you'd absorbed every part of me. When I was away from you, I ached for a sight of you. I couldn't wait to get back to London to see you, hear your voice.'

She listened intently. So much had been hidden from her, she realised now. Gideon had been keeping all this from her. She had wondered why he kept on seeing her when he did not seem to care anything for her. All this had been going on under his cool, deceptive surface, and he had kept it from her.

'I was going crazy keeping my hands off you,' he said thickly. 'I wanted you so much.'

She turned her head to eye him with dislike and cold anger. 'You've got a one-track mind.'

'It wasn't like that,' he protested.

'No?' She lifted her brows, smiling icily.

He looked at her as if she were a stranger, wincing. 'I was torn between wanting to touch you, hold you, and wanting to keep you just as you were.' His eyes softened to a deep tenderness, and she thought of him lying on the grass up on the hill from which the grave circle stared down over the green valleys. She had looked at his sleeping face and seen strength and tenderness in it. She had been blind to the self-willed arrogance which formed that strength.

'Then you suddenly stopped seeing me,' Gideon said through taut white lips. His face had changed; all angles, the bones jutting out from beneath the skin and making him look as though he were suffering acute pain. He stared at her, his dark eyes tense. 'At first I didn't believe it and then when I realised you just didn't want to see me, I went out of my mind. Why did you? Why did you shut me out?'

Marina couldn't answer. Her voice just would not come. She was staring at him and seeing again the dark frustration he had shown her on the night of that concert when he had looked at her across the hall with leaping eyes and the passionate, hungry concentration of a man at the end of his tether. The mask had come off that night. Gideon had shown her naked pain as he looked at her and she was seeing it now, the black eyes tortured with it.

'That boy,' he demanded, his taut lips scarcely moving, the words coming out dry and husky. 'What was there between you and that boy? I took Diana to the theatre one night and I saw you with him.'

'I saw you,' she said bitterly. She had seen him with Diana and she had been so jealous she had wanted to die, but Gideon wasn't thinking of that. He was staring at her, but his eyes were blind as if he were seeing it all again.

'I'd begun to think of you as mine, as belonging to me, without ever realising it. The very fact that I'd never touched you made you so special, put you in a category of your own. Then I saw him put his arm round you and I was almost sick on the spot.'

He broke off, his voice harsh. 'I couldn't bear to imagine what must be going on between the two of you. If he touched you in public I thought he had to be doing more than that in private. I thought of him kissing you, holding you, and I went so pale

Diana noticed and asked me if I felt ill. I told her I did.'

'You were still sleeping with her,' Marina accused fiercely, looking at him with contempt.

She saw from the compression of his mouth, the hardness of his eyes, that he would have lied to her if he dared, but she held his stare and in the end he said grimly: 'Yes, until that night.'

He saw her face close up and her eyes fill with anger and broke out hoarsely, 'I'd never let myself think of you that way! Don't you understand? After the day I came down here and you played to me, I wouldn't allow myself to put a finger on you. I still slept with Diana because it had never meant a damned thing and it didn't seem to me then to have any connection with how I felt about you.'

'That's very comforting,' she said icily.

'Don't, darling,' Gideon muttered.

'Don't call me darling!' She turned to walk away, her body shaking with anger and pain, and he caught her back and held her, putting his cheek down on her hair, the warmth of his breath drifting across her forehead.

'It never happened again after that night, Marina.'

'Don't lie to me,' she said savagely.

'I'm not! That night was the end. I went back to my flat alone and I sat up all night and tried to think, to work out what was happening to me. I still hadn't realised I loved you. I couldn't think, though. My brain wouldn't operate, my heart kept pounding, I was sweating—I felt ill. All I could think of was that I'd lost you, had never had you, that maybe you were somewhere in his arms.' He had perspiration glistening on his skin now at the memory and his eyes were haunted.

'I should have been,' she said in cold bitterness.

She felt the stricken flinch he gave. 'Don't say that.' His arms caught her and held her tightly. 'I couldn't bear it. That night I was in hell. And afterwards it didn't get any better. I couldn't eat, couldn't sleep. I worked—that was all I could do. I worked like a madman. Music had always been the most important thing in my life, but I'd never needed it the way I did then. It was the only way out for me. I played to forget you and I couldn't forget you, so it all went into my music.'

Marina had felt it, heard it, surging in the music; a wild passion which had misery in it. She had recognised the power of the emotions without ever identifying it as anything to do with herself that night.

'I travelled around as usual, but I can't remember anything that happened while I was away from you. I wouldn't let myself face what had happened to me.' His mouth writhed in a bitter mimicry of humour. 'I was scared stiff. I was afraid that if you found out how I felt you'd somehow have power over me, that you'd own me the way my mother had done, smother me.'

She had known that. His admission held no surprise for her. She stood quietly listening, her face sombre.

'But I was sick for you, obsessed with a need to see you. When I got back to London I sent you some tickets for a concert because I had to see you, even if it was only across a hall, and I was afraid that if I rang you up to ask you out you'd refuse.'

She would have refused, of course. Trapped in her own painful fight to forget him, she would have refused and suffered in doing so.

'Then you came with him,' said Gideon in that harsh voice. 'I knew you'd come, I felt you there, I played to you, I said all the things I couldn't say and I knew you heard me. But when I looked at you, you looked the same. I'd thought there would be a change in you, something visible which would tell me what he meant to you, what had happened between you. I had to know.' He broke off and then said thickly, 'If you loved him I had to know.'

'What if I had?' she asked, moving her head to look at him, her eyes trying to read his face.

His eyes burned. 'I didn't think past the fact that I had to know. And when I asked you if you loved him and you didn't answer, I looked round at you and something in your face told me I could have you.'

That stung, it pierced her like a burning knife. She tried to pull away and he wouldn't let her go; his body shook as he held her. 'Don't be angry. I didn't plan it. I didn't take you there meaning that to happen, I swear I didn't, darling. The moment I had you in my arms I just went crazy. My whole body went wild. I had to have you. I stopped think-ing and just . . .'

'Just took what you wanted,' she said with biting contempt. 'As you always have done. That's all that matters, isn't it, Gideon? What you want is the only thing that matters. You've never asked yourself what all this did to me, what I went through during those months?'

He looked stunned, his face blank, and she saw that she had been right. Gideon had never asked himself how she felt, what she had suffered even before she lost the baby and was so ill.

'What do you think was happening to me all this time?' she asked icily. 'Or did you imagine that I was so stupid I had no ideas in my head at all, no feelings to be hurt?'

He stared down at her, the black eyes intent. Slowly he said, 'You were so young, so utterly innocent. I didn't think it would ever have entered your head to feel anything but friendship for me.' His hand lifted to stroke her cheek slowly. 'What did you feel, Marina?' he asked in a low, husky voice.

She caught the eager gleam of the dark eyes and saw the trap in time. Gideon wanted her to admit she had loved him. His eyes had taken on that watchful, excited brightness and his mouth was being held in check by an effort of will.

'All you cared about, all you've ever cared about, was your own feelings, your own desires. I should have avoided you like the plague from the day we met.'

She hadn't, though. She had yielded, helplessly, tempted by her own craving for him and weak in the face of his burning desire for her.

'You had no right to touch me,' she broke out bitterly.

'I knew that,' he muttered grimly, self-contemptuously. 'But at the time all I thought about was satisfying my own need for you.'

Her eyes reinforced her biting contempt and he registered it with a compression of the mouth. 'I did love you,' he insisted. 'I just wouldn't admit it, even to myself. I told myself that it was a crazy infatuation which would end one day. I thought it was just frustrated desire and that when I'd had you I wouldn't want you any more.'

That was what she had thought, too, and it had hurt her badly. During those weeks she had been miserable and in despair, and Gideon hadn't even been aware of her feelings. He had never in his life been aware of anything but his own emotions. He had never considered for a moment what he might be doing to her.

'Why did you marry me?' she asked bitingly. 'You could just have paid me off, agreed to support the baby.'

His eyes closed and his skin paled. 'Don't! You know why I married you—I wanted to marry you. My God, Marina, I jumped at the chance!'

'Do you expect me to believe that?'

His eyes opened and he looked at her with haunted self-contempt. 'Don't you understand? When you vanished like that and I couldn't find out where you were I began to suspect you'd gone away with somebody else. I went crazy. I was so jealous and miserable I wanted to die. Then Grandie told me the truth and I saw at once that I could marry you without ever admitting how badly I needed you.'

She could only stare at him dumbly. That had been a terrible time for her, pregnant and afraid of the future, aching for his love and knowing she did not have it, and all that Gideon had thought about was himself, as usual.

'You really are a swine, aren't you?' she said with a slow bitter distaste.

He ran a hand over his face as if trying to pull himself together. She saw the long fingers trembling as they moved.

'Don't hate me, darling,' he groaned. 'I know I deserve it, but don't, because I've paid for it all.' His hand came down and he caught at her, pulled her into his arms, kissing her hair, her eyes, her cheeks. 'I realise now how you've suffered and I wish I could have been the only one to go through hell, but I did suffer, Marina. When I saw you lying in that road and I thought you were dead I went out of my mind. And this last year without you has been the worst year of my life.' His lips moved down the curve of her cheek to reach her mouth and she pushed him away violently.

'Don't touch me!'

'Marina,' he muttered hoarsely, trying to take her back into his arms.

'I mean it!' Her white face was acid. 'You don't love me—you never have. You wouldn't know how to love. Frustrated desire was all you ever felt for me, and it's all you feel now.' She looked him up and down, her eyes contemptuous. 'And I don't love you. If anything I despise you. You're a selfish, contemptible swine!'

Gideon's face hardened and whitened until the black eyes were a slash of lightless intensity.

Marina turned and walked out of the room. The room was so still and quiet that she could hear the muted violence of his breathing, the smothered drag of his lungs as they functioned in a painful physical necessity. It had given her a tortured pleasure to say that to him, to be aware that she had finally hurt him as deeply as he had ever hurt her.

She sat in her room and listened to the slow whisper of the sea. No human being has the right to put his own desires in front of the happiness of anyone else. Gideon's brilliance did not give him that right.

She stared at her own hands, seeing the surface tension of her skin, the outline of the bones beneath that, the shaping supporting flesh which one could not see. One took so much for granted. The daily miracle of life aroused little amazement and wonder in most people until they had to face the threat of losing it. When she walked out of the flat that day she had not even seen that car because the whole of her being was concentrated on the agony of what she had just seen, the realisation that Gideon did not love her, had never loved her, because if he had he would not have been making love to Diana Grenoby.

She had not cared if she lost her life. Perhaps she had even subconsciously but deliberately walked under that car, knowing what she was doing. Accidents are not always so very accidental. People take crazy risks because they do not care what happens to them.

Gideon had driven her to the very edge of despair. Now he imagined that by telling her he loved her he was wiping the slate clean. He was wrong. Even if he was telling the truth and had not had a secret affair with Diana during their marriage, his silence on the subject of his feelings indicated all too clearly that Gideon still put his own needs in front of those of anybody else. That wasn't love.

It had not been merely that her own life had almost been thrown away. She had lost her baby and she knew she carried the scar of guilt for that—guilt and resentment because it had been Gideon's fault that she walked under that car. He had killed the baby and he had killed something vital inside herself; a trust, a warmth she would never feel again.

Gideon had never been prepared to risk admitting his feelings because he had half expected that one day he would stop feeling the way he did. He had admitted it. He had believed that once he had satisfied his desire for her he would lose interest. And maybe he had been right. One day he might well have stopped wanting her, and then she would have found herself being thrust out of his life without compunction. Gideon had known that, expected it, and yet he had married her, without stopping to think what damage it would do to her when he grew tired of her.

A deep flush grew on her cheekbones as she remembered the argument he had had with Diana. She had watched and known that some violent emotion was churning inside the other woman. She had watched as Gideon coldly, angrily, pushed the other woman aside, irritated boredom in his hard face. She had seen all that and had not known that she was seeing just how ruthless Gideon could be in such personal relationships. That had been herself she had been watching without knowing it. He would have walked away from her with just that look of icy indifference and she would have been left like a broken doll with no hope and no comfort.

'Aren't you coming to lunch?' he asked from the door, and she turned her pale head to look at him with undisguised hatred and contempt. Her eyes were alive with the imagined agony of what Gideon could do to her, might have done, had in a sense done.

He saw that look and his whiteness deepened, the lines around eye and mouth bitten into his taut flesh.

'Don't look at me like that,' he cried harshly.

'If you don't like the way I look at you, you have an option. Go and don't come back.'

'I can't,' he groaned, his hands hanging loosely by his side and that pain in his dark eyes. 'I love you.'

He had refused to commit himself to her once and now she read the total capitulation in his face. She had doubted if he loved her once, but she did not doubt it now. Gideon turned the force of his feeling on her and it shrivelled her like fire, the pain and heat of it making her shrink. She turned her head away because now she did not want to know. She was empty. Pain had made her so sensitive that a finger laid on her skin could make her wince. She did not want to face or accept Gideon's love or his pain. He had no right to either.

'I don't care,' Marina said flatly. 'Just go. You're boring me.'

CHAPTER NINE

GIDEON turned and walked away without answering, but she did not need to see his face to know that she had got another dart home. She had heard the bitter intake of his breath, felt the protest he had not spoken but which had hovered on his pale lips.

So short a time ago she had been a trustful, confiding child who had felt no fear of the dark stranger crashing into her life. Now she sat on the edge of the bed, listening as Gideon walked heavily down the stairs, and felt a savage pleasure in having hurt him again.

When one is innocent of pain, of the havoc it can wreak, one is never cruel. Cruelty is born of pain, of a need to hurt in turn. Marina looked at her own reflection in the mirror and did not much like what she saw. She had liked the self she had thought she saw a few days ago. Now she looked at the taut-faced woman staring at her and shivered in rejection.

The lines of maturity she could now see had been etched in her face by experiences she only wanted to forget. She was still young, a girl more than a woman. That was why she had never seen any disturbing signs to warn her that she was not the eighteen-year-old she believed herself to be. At just twenty-two there was little difference in her looks. It was the eyes, the expression, which was now changed. With memory pain had come back and with pain had come those carved lines which Gideon had given her.

She went downstairs and Grandie was in the kitchen alone. He looked round searchingly. 'All right?'

She smiled and touched her forehead to his shoulder, nodding. He patted her back clumsily.

'Hungry?' he asked.

Marina looked at the salad. 'Yes,' she said, and was surprised to find that it was true. They sat down and made a good meal, having cold ham with the salad and fresh fruit to follow the meal. Gideon did not appear and she decided not to ask Grandie if he had gone. She would discover that in time and she was in no hurry to find out.

They cleared the table together and washed up, then Grandie asked her with a faint hesitation to play for him. She gave him a rueful smile, guessing that he was still hoping to arouse her ambition and her love of music.

She played a Chopin nocturne for him and the music fitted her mood, quiet and sad, an elegiac piece of music with a thread of wry resignation in it. She gazed out of the window while she played. Grandie sat so quietly that she could only just hear him breathing. His pride in her made her sadder than ever. She wished that for him she could have somehow learnt to desire fame, learnt to enjoy the battleground of the concert hall.

When she stopped playing Grandie got up and

kissed her, as he often did, wordless, slightly elevated, needing now to be alone. He would have given the world to see her take his place in the concert hall.

There were other ways in which she could use her ability, she thought. The garish lightning that played around the head of the solo performer might terrify her, but she could happily fit into other forms of music. She liked playing as an accompanist. Letting her fingers drift over the keyboard she considered the various possibilities. She would talk to Grandie before she made up her mind. Although she was primarily a pianist she could play the violin to a certain standard. If the worst came to the worst she might get work teaching music in a school. She would have to go back to college for a final year, but that would be a pleasant experience.

There was no sign of Gideon when she joined Grandie in the kitchen later. She still did not ask Grandie if Gideon had gone. Instead she asked him what he thought of her idea of going back to college for a year before looking for a job in music. Grandie's face lit up and she saw that he had not relinquished his hopes for her future.

'I think it would be an excellent idea.'

'Do you think they would take me back?'

He laughed quietly. 'Oh, I think we'd persuade them.' Grandie still had pull and Marina's own ability had been demonstrated clearly enough during her time at the college.

'I could accompany,' she said, looking at him carefully.

His face was as careful. 'Yes, of course you could,

he agreed in an easy, casual voice, and she was not deceived. Grandie wasn't giving up yet. He wanted to get her back into that milieu—he believed that once she had the taste of that life in her mouth she wouldn't be able to relinquish it.

She went to bed early, leaving Grandie sitting in the kitchen playing a slow game of Patience. The wind had risen and the floorboards creaked and moaned, the windows rattling, the sound of the sea loud, as though it were just below her room. She fell asleep almost at once, though, lulled by the sounds of the night.

She woke realising that it was still dark, the wind louder than ever, lashing around the house in a fit of frenzy, the sea thundering close at hand and the sound of rain dashing against the windows. A storm had blown up while she slept. She lay listening to the unleashed violence and then sat up, ears pricked, hearing another sound. Was that Grandie still downstairs?

She looked at the clock. Two o'clock. A frown crossed her forehead. Was Grandie ill? The sounds were muffled by the wind and rain, but there was definitely someone moving about downstairs.

Slipping out of bed, she put on her wrap and tiptoed down the stairs. When she pushed open the kitchen door the figure standing there turned to look at her and she stared back at him.

He was drenched, his black hair flat on his head, his face gleaming with rain. He had stripped off his sweater and shirt and her startled eyes ran over the lean, muscled body briefly before she looked back at his face.

mingled with the faint astringent fragrance of Gideon's body.

Marina put on the kettle and got out cups. Gideon came back in a clean sweater and trousers. She could see that he had combed down his hair. It no longer stood in those ruffled peaks but lay smooth and partially damp across his head. The rain and wind had given a glowing colour to his skin, but the dark eyes were sombre under their black brows.

'Have you eaten?' she asked with her back to him.

'I'm not hungry.' He moved quietly until he stood just behind her. 'I'm sorry I woke you.'

'You didn't,' she shrugged without turning round. 'The storm woke me. Is it very rough at sea?'

'Waves like mountains,' he told her. 'I saw them breaking over the jetty, higher than houses.'

'We don't often get seas like that. I wouldn't like to be out at sea tonight.'

'No,' he agreed, so close that she could hear his breathing and the faint sounds of his tiniest movements, the rasp of his hands as he pushed them into his pockets, the rustle of his collar against his throat as he turned his head.

The kettle boiled and she made the tea, her actions deft and quick, the automatic movements which the hands can perform while the brain is absorbed in other things. Gideon watched her and she knew what he was feeling. She was deeply aware of what was going on inside him because it was a response to what was happening inside her.

They were talking like polite strangers, but underneath that their bodies were vibrating with the

powerful tug of physical attraction and she could
not stop the process.

'You must eat something,' she told him briskly.
'I'll make you a ham sandwich.' He watched her as
she deftly cut the bread and buttered it, laid the
ham inside. She pushed the plate of sandwiches
across to Gideon.

He sat at the kitchen table and looked at the food.
'I'm really not hungry,' he muttered.

'Eat it.' She poured the tea and gave him a cup.
Reluctantly he began to eat one of the sandwiches.

He fiddled with the edge of the plate, studying
the pretty band of roses with apparent fascination.
'What are you going to do, Marina?'

She sat down and sipped her tea without answering and Gideon lifted his black head to look at her.

She met his eyes. 'Grandie and I were discussing
that today. I think I'll go back to college for my final
year.'

Gideon looked back at the food and pushed the
plate away. 'I see,' he muttered.

She had never seen him so muted, the inner light
of his powerful personality completely doused. His
mouth was set in lines of wry acceptance. She could
not see his eyes, they were hidden by their lids, but
the lashes flickered constantly.

He picked up his cup and the sound of it jarring
against the saucer told her that his hand was shaking. He held it between both hands and sipped the
tea, still not looking at her.

Pain pulsed inside her. She did not want to respond to the silent appeal he was making, she did

not want to be aware of his pain. Gideon had no right to feel it.

'You were right,' he said suddenly, his voice husky. 'I've been blindly selfish all along. I'd never seen it all from your angle. I'd only ever seen it from mine.'

'You don't need to tell me that,' she said bitterly.

'No.' His head bowed lower. 'You despise me, and I deserve it. I accept that I've been selfish.' He lifted his head abruptly and the dark eyes looked straight into hers. 'But that day you came to the flat and saw me with Diana, I wasn't kissing her, Marina. She was kissing me, and if you'd come in a moment later you wouldn't have seen what you did. I didn't want her to kiss me. Hell, I was indifferent to her. I hadn't seen her since the night I saw you and that boy together—I swear that on my honour.'

'Your honour?' She laughed and he winced.

'I don't deserve *that*,' he emphasised. 'I wouldn't lie to you. You've got to believe me.'

She studied him and she knew she did believe him. Diana's angry passion when they met the other day had told her that Gideon had dismissed the other woman from his life with cold finality. She felt pity for Diana. Gideon had been ruthless with her. Once he had made up his mind, he had cut her from his life without looking back. Diana had never meant a thing to him.

He saw the realisation in her face and hurriedly went on, 'I was working on those damned papers in the flat because I was desperate to get down here to you. My God, Marina, I was aching to see you. The last thing on my mind was Diana. She just walked in and took me by surprise. She'd heard I was in town alone.' He grimaced, breaking off, a dark colour invading his cheeks. 'Diana thought . . .'

'I can guess what she thought,' Marina said drily.

Diana had come because she hoped that Gideon would have grown tired of his marriage and might be prepared to resume his relationship with her. Past experience of his brief romances would have given her grounds for hoping. Poor Diana, Marina thought; it was painful to love without a hope of return, and she was sure Diana loved him.

'Have you ever realised what you've done to her?' she asked him bitterly. 'She has feelings too, you know.'

His face was set and dark. 'She almost lost me the one thing I've ever cared about,' he said through his teeth. 'She just wouldn't accept that I didn't want her and because of that you almost died.' He stopped speaking, his throat moving in a convulsive swallow. 'I thought for a while you might die. I'd have killed her if I'd seen her!'

There was a silence. She could hear him breathing, the rough sound abrasive. The wind roared past the window and the latch clattered. Marina jumped, her nerves stretched to the point where every little noise could pierce her brain.

'It's only the wind,' Gideon said gently.

She drank some of her tea but it had grown cold and tasted flat and vile. Gideon watched her, his dark eyes intent. 'I thought until my head ached,' he said. 'Diana was a red herring, wasn't she? It wasn't Diana who split us up, it was me. I ruined what we could have had. If I hadn't been so obsessed with protecting myself I'd have realised what I was doing to you.'

She looked back at him, her breathing stilled, seeing a change in his face, a look almost of humility which seemed odd on that hard, powerful mask of his.

'Did you love me?' he asked huskily.

She didn't reply, just stared at him.

'You did, didn't you?' He smiled oddly, wry self-contempt in the movement of his mouth. 'And I never stopped to think, to ask myself what was going on inside your head. I was too busy struggling with my own feelings to ask how you felt. I was so afraid of losing myself that I lost you.'

In the silence she heard the clock ticking and the wind lashing across the sea, the slow sift of the ash inside the stove.

'I suppose I knew you had to find me attractive,' Gideon muttered. 'You wouldn't have slept with me otherwise. But I wouldn't let myself ask you if you loved me because by asking that I would have admitted the whole question of love, and that was the one thing I didn't dare to do.' He put out his hand and caught hers, took it to his lips, staring at her. 'Do you still love me, Marina?'

'How can I?' she asked flatly. 'You've told me too much about yourself that makes you unlovable.' His hand tightened on her fingers in a wince. She went on quietly, 'You may love me now, or think you do, but in a year, two, you may decide you've stopped loving me, and then I would be another Diana to be kicked out of your life.'

'No,' he said. 'No. I've never cared for anyone but

you. I wouldn't do that to you. I may have fought against loving you, but I've given in, Marina. I'll love you to the end of my life.'

'How can I believe that?' she asked angrily.

'You must,' he muttered.

She pulled her hand from his grip and stood up. Gideon got up, too, catching her arm.

'Don't go. Listen to me.'

'Why should I?'

Their eyes met and quarrelled violently, a dark pleading in his, a cold rejection in hers. Gideon moved closer and Marina glanced away from the magnetic pull of his lean body, the physical attraction she knew very well she could still feel throbbing away inside herself. It was a vital part of love, but it was only a part. There had to be a lot more than that if love was to survive. How did she know that Gideon felt any more than an urgent desire for her?

'I tried to start again,' he told her huskily. 'When I came down here this time it was because I was going mad not seeing you. Grandie had asked me to stay away, but I couldn't.'

Her eyes angrily told him how selfish that had been and his grew hard with an admission of his realisation of it.

'But when I saw that you didn't remember me, I thought it would give me the chance to make things happen as they should have happened in the beginning. If I'd admitted I'd fallen in love with you right from the start, I'd have come down here to court you, to make you fall in love with me. I'd have married you and none of this would have happened.

I tried to reshape our lives. I wanted to love you and let you see it. I wanted to teach you to love me.'

And he had succeeded, of course. She had fallen in love with him all over again. The moment she saw him she had felt that tug of deep attraction. Her mind might not have known him, but her body had, and it had moved like a sleepwalker into his arms, wildly responsive to every touch, every kiss.

She looked away, her skin flushing deeply, and Gideon stared at her fixedly, piercing the defences she was trying to erect against the probe of his stare.

'Think about it, darling,' he whispered, watching her.

She lifted her head, her eyes flashing. 'I can tell you now what I think. I think it would have been better for me if I'd never laid eyes on you. I think you've given me as much pain as any one human being can stand, and I don't want to see you again. I think that you should get out of my life and stay out!'

He had gone white again, the black eyes fixed and hard. His mouth was held steady, but she saw the muscle jerking betrayingly beside the stiff lines of it.

She was already subsiding from her angry excitement, her body trembling. 'Go away,' she muttered, not looking at him.

She felt him watching her. He laughed harshly. 'I might as well burn my last boat,' he said oddly, and before she had had time to work out what he meant, he had caught her into his arms and his mouth was covering hers, the hungry burning demand of his kiss destroying all her defences, sending a wave of violent passion pouring through her.

His arms locked round her and the kiss deepened, draining her whole body until she lay limply against him, feeling the urgent pressure of his body growing as he sensed her weakness.

He lifted his head at last and looked down at her flushed face with a gleam in the dark eyes. 'Goodnight, my darling.'

She couldn't believe it as he turned and walked away. He knew what had just happened inside her. He had felt it, all the helpless, hungry response she had not been able to control. But he was going.

She stood there, listening to his footsteps on the stairs, trying to make sense of it. If he had wished Gideon could have pressed her to the ultimate surrender. She had put up no resistance and he had been completely aware of it. Why had he gone?

She tied her wrap tightly around her, her neck bent in a defensive weakness. Gideon was a strategist; he had done this deliberately. She went around the room, tidying it for the night, then went up to her room and climbed into bed. Sleep evaded her for a long time and when she did finally fall into an uneasy doze it was dawn, the sky pale and windfretted.

She slept until late in the morning. Grandie did not disturb her. When she eventually struggled downstairs he looked at her quickly.

'How do you feel?'

'Fine,' she said too brightly.

He nodded. 'What would you like for breakfast?'

'I'll get myself some toast,' she told him, moving to cut the bread. Casually she asked: 'Gideon up?'

'He's gone,' said Grandie, and her hand shook.
The bread knife slipped and she gave a faint cry.
Grandie came hurrying over in distress and stared
at the dark red blood seeping from the cut.

He can't do this to me, Marina thought in a sick
anguish. I hate him! How could he go like that? He
didn't even say goodbye.

Grandie held her hand under the cold tap, watching her white face. 'Does it hurt much?'

It hurt like hell, but she smiled and said: 'No,'
because the pain she was feeling had nothing to do
with her cut hand.

She knew, of course. She had known last night as
her whole body shook in response to his hands and
mouth. She wanted him. Whatever he had done,
might do, to her, she wanted him. And Gideon had
known. She had seen the look in those dark eyes and
had been aware that she had betrayed herself finally
and for ever. Gideon knew how she felt. Yet he had
gone away.

I hate him, she thought. I hate him!

CHAPTER TEN

LATER she walked along the cliffs, watching the conflict in the skies, the wind driving the clouds across the horizon, the sea tossing and turning like an uneasy sleeper, with points of light glittering across its troubled surface as the sun slid in and out of the windblown clouds.

For all his brilliance as a musician, Gideon had been stunted in his emotional growth in childhood; unable to co-ordinate the demands of body and heart, like an autistic child which never makes the right connections and is isolated from those around him by his own self-obsessed internal life. Children are imprinted with the lessons of life from their earliest years. They learn from their parents how to give and receive love. It is the necessary lesson which they must learn if they are to do more than exist in an emotional vacuum inhabited only by themselves.

Gideon's body had learnt to desire the pleasure women could give, but his heart and mind had rejected them because of his mother's stifling possessiveness. He had grown up seeing life from that narrow angle, the obsessive camera eye which only focused on a limited objective—his own desire.

When he met Marina his first instinct had been

to reach out and take her, as he always reached out for what he wanted. She saw now that in checking that involuntary urge right at the start Gideon had been beginning to learn to love. The change had begun in him even then, but he hadn't known it, and he had hidden it from her because he was confused and frightened by the strange new feelings inside him.

Staring across the tossing sea, she admitted to herself that Gideon loved her and that the measure of his ability to love was reflected in the very strength and duration of his fight against it. She had seen for herself how his feelings for her had invaded his music, given to the barren brilliance of his cleverness a deep and profound emotion which changed it completely.

But he had gone. Why? Why after wringing that yielding passion out of her, despite all her angry protests, had he walked out like that?

She turned to walk back to the cottage, shivering, and stopped dead in her tracks as she saw the tall, lean figure in grey pants and a rollneck blue sweater.

He looked into her eyes and smiled. 'Windy, isn't it?'

She couldn't find the voice to answer him, staring at him. He had come back. The wind whipped through his dark hair, sending it flying in rough peaks.

He ran his hand through it to rake it down. 'What's your name?'

For a moment she could only stare, bewildered and uncomprehending, then her face flooded with colour and her voice said huskily, 'Marina.'

He moved closer, staring down at her. 'Marina,' he murmured. 'Child of the sea. It suits you. Has anyone ever told you that your hair is like moonlight?'

She looked away, her lashes flickering on her cheek. 'I've been warned never to talk to strangers.'

'That's easily remedied,' he told her softly. 'My name is Gideon.'

'I'm too old for games,' she said in faintly sad protest.

'This is far too serious to be called a game.' He touched her cheek with the back of his hand. 'Love always is, Marina.'

'I thought you'd gone,' she whispered.

'I'll never go. How can I? How far would I get without my heart?'

She laughed involuntarily, but he was staring at her mouth and the expression in the dark eyes ended her laughter. He slowly bent his head and kissed her lightly.

'You're very beautiful.'

Her heart was beating far too fast. She drew back and walked on with Gideon walking beside her, suiting the long strides to her pace. The wind tossed their hair and bent the trees. The sea rushed up on to the rocky beach below.

'I love you,' Gideon said quietly. 'You're the breath of my life, the beat of my heart. I can't go because I couldn't live without you. I know—I've tried during the past year, and although I may have walked and talked as if I were alive, inside I've been dead. The way I felt about you didn't stop while we were apart, it got stronger. It's got stronger every day since the day we met. Three years is a long time, Marina. If my feelings weren't deep they wouldn't have lasted three years. I haven't thought of anything but you all the time we've been apart.'

She didn't answer, but she sighed as she accepted that. Three years was a long time.

'Why did you go last night?' she asked without looking at him.

He laughed softly. 'I was tempted to stay, but I didn't want to make another mistake. I wanted you to have time to think.'

'You didn't give me much time,' she pointed out.

'No? It seems like centuries to me,' Gideon said in a husky whisper. 'My God, I wanted to stay, Marina.'

She stopped and their eyes met, then she was in his arms, clinging, their bodies pressed together and their mouths exchanging an abandoned passion which made her heart beat like a metronome.

He moved his mouth softly against her cheek when their lips parted and sighed. 'Tell me one thing, darling. If you loved me why did you stop seeing me and go around with that boy?'

'I didn't want to get hurt,' she said, and felt the harsh intake of breath he gave.

'Oh, God,' he muttered. 'Darling, my darling! I hate myself for what I've done to you. I deserve to lose you.'

She moved her head back and considered him soberly. 'I was too young for you,' she decided wryly.

'No,' he said at once, his face harsh.

'Far too young,' she murmured, a smile coming

into her eyes. 'I didn't know what sort of animal I'd caught.'

His eyes relaxed, the lines which had appeared around his mouth softening, and he grinned at her. 'A wild one, I'm afraid.'

'Savage,' she agreed, her eyes teasing him.

'But tameable,' he suggested, a glint coming into the dark eyes.

'Do you think so?' She looked up at him impudently. 'I'm not so sure. I don't know if I have a cage big enough.'

'I shan't need a cage,' he promised. 'I'll never try to escape.'

She had been a child when he first seduced her and all their lovemaking had been silent, heated, secretive. Gideon had been unwilling to speak too much for fear of what he might let slip and Marina had been too uncertain, too shy, to say much. She realised that their marriage had never been real until now. They had never communicated beyond the fierce abandon of their lovemaking. They had a lot to learn about each other. She was a woman now. It had been a painful and difficult growing up but it was over now. She looked at Gideon and wondered if he knew how far they had both come in the past year when they were apart. They had each taken a silent, bitter journey into themselves, but they had returned, like characters in a fairy story, with miraculous discoveries.

Gideon knew from her face that dark thoughts were passing through her head. He held her tightly, his strong body sheltering her from the onslaught of the cruel wind.

'Don't shut me out,' he said huskily. 'What's wrong? Don't you believe me? You must believe me, Marina.'

'I do,' she said. 'I love you, Gideon.'

His mouth shook slightly. 'Darling,' he muttered, lowering his head to search for her mouth again.

All the cold chill, the pain and uncertainty, had fallen away. They had to learn to forget the past. An obsession with past pain could be as dangerous as any other.

They walked back to the cottage hand in hand. 'I've got a tour coming up, I'm afraid,' Gideon admitted. 'I don't want to go, but I've agreed to and I can't let people down. Will you come, Marina?' His hand held hers possessively. 'I don't want to leave you behind again.'

'Of course I'll come,' she said lightly. 'Try and leave me!'

He laughed, looking sideways with a glimmer of amusement.

'I shall haunt you like a ghost,' she teased.

'You have for months,' he muttered.

'We're not going to talk about what's over,' she said with a crisp command that made him smile again.

'No,' he accepted.

'This is a new beginning.'

'Yes,' said Gideon, and something in his tone made her look at him with quick comprehension.

'I wonder if Grandie is out,' he said softly, and laughed as her colour rose. He grinned at her. 'I saw him trotting off to the village as I arrived. He gave me a funny look.'

'The way you come and go I'm not surprised!'

'I'll never go again,' he whispered, kissing her cheek. 'You'll never get rid of me, Marina. I mean to stick like glue.'

The cottage was silent and empty, the wind roaring round it in a constant howl which made the trees lash to and fro and the windows rattle.

He held her cradled against his heart, kissing her passionately. 'Tell me you love me.'

'I told you,' she said, opening drowsy eyes which held an inviting smile, watching the blaze of responsive hunger growing in his dark eyes.

'Tell me again,' he said huskily.

She said it in a soft sensual voice, watching his colour deepen and his eyes darken.

'Oh, God,' he groaned as he pulled her down on to the bed. 'I love you, darling.'

He lost control from that moment. All the cool, clever processes of his brain ceased to function. He touched her with hands that trembled, his heart so fast she could hear its pounding as he moved against her, and his face was taut with a hunger which was driving both of them. He made love to her as if all his life went into the satisfaction of that need. He had abandoned all his defences, eager to show her openly how much he cared. Her hands caressed the smooth cool back, meeting his demand with her own, the supple movements of her slender body bringing gasps of agonised pleasure from him. They had never made love like this before. Gideon's hoarse cries of love had an abandonment which gave him to her finally and for ever.

They slept afterwards for an hour, a sheet thrown

over their bodies, and when Marina yawned and opened her eyes she found Gideon still sleeping but with his arms clamped round her as though he were afraid to let her go even in sleep.

She tickled his cheek and his lashes flickered upward. He looked at her dazedly and she smiled.

He closed his eyes again, sighing. 'I thought it was another dream,' he said. 'There've been so many.'

'I remember,' she said drily, and he grinned at that, a wicked amusement coming into his face.

'Shameless of you,' he teased. 'Walking into my room like that and handing yourself to me on a plate!'

'If you'd had any principles you would never have taken me,' she pointed out.

He sobered. 'I was a starving man given a chance to eat,' he groaned. 'I couldn't let the chance slip.'

She snuggled closer. 'It was good, wasn't it?'

He let his lips drift over her hair. 'It was heaven.'

'I was so horrified in the morning. I remembered every second of it, and although I thought I'd dreamt it I was terrified of seeing you again.'

She felt him smiling. 'I enjoyed the way you looked at me when you came down to breakfast. You gave me such a shy, sheepish look and I was hard put to it not to get up and kiss you there and then.'

'I'd have been overcome with shock,' she said, her eyes dancing. 'I could barely look at you as it was.'

'So I noticed.' He bent his head and kissed her shoulder. 'You were very sweet and I could scarcely keep my hands off you.'

'I don't remember it like that,' she commented. He had kissed her the day after he arrived. It had been a tentative kiss. He had been carefully testing the ice before he walked on to it, but she had not rejected him and Gideon had moved fast after that.

He read the thoughts in her face and laughed. 'You were very responsive, my love.'

'And you were very unprincipled!'

'I love you,' he whispered, finding her mouth. 'I had to get close to you. I needed to be with you. When we first met we were different people, darling. I was a different person. I'm not the man I was— you've changed me. Coming down and realising that you didn't know me, I saw that if I trod carefully I could find the way to reach you as I'd never reached you before, and it worked. You were open and warm and responsive and if I'd thought I loved you before I soon loved you fifty times more.'

Marina laid her head on his chest and heard the steady deep beat of his heart. They lay in silence for a few moments, their bodies close, then they heard movements downstairs and Gideon groaned.

'Grandie's back. Why couldn't he take another hour?'

'We must go down and tell him,' she said, sighing.

'I think he already knows,' said Gideon in a dry voice.

She laughed. 'Yes.' Grandie knew. There had never been any doubt that Marina loved Gideon and for all her anger and hurt, Grandie had been aware of that. She had talked of going back to college, taking up a career, but Grandie had known secretly that everything in her that was alive was turned towards Gideon. Gideon was not the only one who was unable to live without a heart. Marina had lost hers to him the day they met, although it had taken her some time to realise it, and she had never seriously believed that she would be able to turn him away.

'I suppose we must go down,' said Gideon reluctantly.

'Yes,' she said again, smiling.

'I'd like to spend the next twenty-four hours in here,' he muttered with a quick look at her.

'Isn't that tough?' she said mockingly, laughing, and slid off the bed before he could grab her. He watched her with dark, intent eyes as she dressed, but she did not look at him because if she did she was afraid she might go back to him and Grandie was waiting.

'Do get dressed, Gideon,' she scolded.

'Kiss me first,' he demanded.

She walked to the door and looked back at him with a teasing smile. 'I'll see you downstairs.'

As she closed the door she heard his exasperated groan and laughed to herself. She might love Gideon, but she had learnt something from their three years together. You don't tame a savage animal by giving it its own way. Gideon still had a lot to learn.

Grandie looked round at her as she entered the kitchen. His face was blank, but she caught the curious flicker of his eyes before he glanced away from her.

'He came back, then,' he said drily.

She put her arms round him and laid her head on his shoulder. 'I'm going back to him.'

Grandie sighed. 'I knew that, of course. It was obvious from the day he turned up.'

'He loves me.' She knew Grandie would worry about that.

He was silent for a moment, then he said harshly: 'I hope so.'

'And I love him.'

'Yes,' he said in a gentler tone.

Grandie accepted that. She would never have entered into that first passionate relationship with Gideon if she had not been crazily in love with him.

She was sorry that once again she had dashed all Grandie's hopes for her, but life only gave you a restricted choice and she had long ago realised that she had made hers the day she first set eyes on Gideon.

'It's fate,' she said half flippantly.

Grandie did not smile. 'Yes,' he agreed, and she could tell he did not think much of fate.

From the music room came the sound of the piano and they both turned to listen, their faces intent.

'Gideon,' said Grandie, unnecessarily.

Only one man played like that—with arrogance and verve yet with a delicacy of touch which was permeated with strong but controlled emotion.

Marina walked away from Grandie and went into the music room. Gideon's long back was towards her as he sat at the piano, his hands moving with their customary assurance while he gazed out of the window. Marina sat down quietly and he flicked her a brief glance over his shoulder. He did not smile, but the dark eyes were passionate. The music swelled into a triumphant cascade, filled with certainty, clear and vibrant with a piercing sweetness. However many times he said: 'I love you,' he would never say it in quite the way he was saying it now. They had come so close to losing each other that all Gideon's joy and relief poured into the sound rippling from beneath his long fingers, and Marina sat and listened to him with happiness in her eyes.

Harlequin Plus

THE LOVE-STRUCK MUSICIANS

Charlotte Lamb's Gideon Firth is certainly not the first musician to have been struck by Cupid's arrow. In fact, many famous pianists and composers throughout the centuries were noted for the passion with which they fell in love.

One such was Franz Liszt, great Hungarian pianist and composer of the last century. Here is a translation from the French of a letter he wrote to Marie d'Agoult, his lady love, in 1835. Hope you enjoy it!

My heart is overflowing with emotion and with happiness! I know not what heavenly languor, what immense and exquisite delight fills and entirely consumes me. It seems to me that I had never loved, never been loved!!! Tell me then whence came this mysterious restlessness, these ineffable forebodings, these divine quivers of love. Oh! this cannot but be from you, sister, angel, woman, Marie!... This cannot be anything but surely just a gentler ray from your fiery soul, or perhaps some secret, agonizing tear, which you left in my breast long ago.

SUPERROMANCE
SUBSCRIPTION
RESERVATION COUPON

Complete and mail TODAY to

Harlequin Reader Service

In the U.S.A.
1440 South Priest Drive
Tempe, AZ 85281

In Canada
649 Ontario Street
Stratford, Ontario N5A 6W2

Please reserve my subscription to the 2 NEW
SUPERROMANCES published every eight weeks
(12 a year). Every eight weeks I will receive
2 NEW SUPERROMANCES at the low price of
$2.50 each (total— $5). There are no shipping and
handling or any other hidden charges, and I am free
to cancel at any time after taking as many or
as few novels as I wish.

NAME_____
(Please Print)

ADDRESS_____

CITY_____

STATE/PROV._____

ZIP/POSTAL CODE_____